# infantry weapons

### John Weeks

BB

Editor-in-Chief: Barrie Pitt
Editor: David Mason
Art Director: Sarah Kingham
Picture Editor: Robert Hunt
Designer: David A Evans
Cover: Denis Piper
Special Drawings: John Batchelor
Photographic Research: Owen Wood
Cartographer: Richard Natkiel

First Printing: August 1971
Printed in United States of America

Ballantine Books Inc.
101 Fifth Avenue New York NY 10003

An Intext Publisher

# Contents

# The last argument

## Introduction by Ian V Hogg

Artillery was once known as 'Ultima Ratio Regis' – 'The Last Argument of Kings'; if that be the case, the last argument of the less exalted soldier is his personal weapon, be it rifle, bayonet, pistol or machine gun. When the generals have planned and the armies have mustered, the artillery has spoken and the armour has manoeuvred, it is the man on the ground with a rifle in his hand who actually occupies the enemy land and, as Colonel Weeks relates, 'winkles the other bastard out of his foxhole and gets him to sign the Peace Treaty'.

Small arms, then, are the weapons which the vast majority of soldiers handle, curse, reminisce about and remember afterwards. They hold an immense fascination for young and old, and the story of their development is full of strange by-ways and interesting revelations. Probably no period saw as much activity in weapon development as the years of the Second World War, and a lot of this activity was in the field of infantry weapons. This period saw the rise of the sub-machine gun, the birth of the assault rifle, and the sunset of the bolt-action magazine rifle, to name but three of the subjects dealt with in this book.

John Weeks is well suited to the task of telling the story of infantry weapons. A Technical Staff Officer of the British Army, he became Director of Studies, Infantry Weapons, at the Royal Military College of Science, and was later Commandant of the Infantry Trials and Development Unit. In these varying roles he has seen, examined, studied and assessed practically every infantry weapon ever made, and has read innumerable reports on inventions, developments and trials all of which furnishes a depth of experience and background denied to most students of this subject. In addition to this technical expertise he has the rare ability to be able to explain it in simple terms and make a technical story turn into a narrative as interesting and compelling as any fictional tale of war.

The tale he unfolds will no doubt surprise many readers, and some of them may be those who, having used the weapons he discusses, might consider themselves familiar with them. The assessments and comments made here are those of a professional infantryman (a paratrooper in fact) who is concerned not with a weapon's appearance or theoretical advantages, but with its ability to function on the battlefield. Indeed, one is led to the conclusion that some actions in the war must have succeeded in spite of the weapons rather than because of them, and there is an interesting parallel to be drawn between a nation's military record and the weapons which it provided for its soldiers which is taken to a splendid conclusion in the foundation of the new science of fusilology.

A theme which runs through much of the development of weapons retailed here is the difficulty of getting a new weapon or concept into actual service use. Some of this was the conservatism for which all armies are justly or unjustly blamed, but much of it was due to the men who held the purse-strings. The First World War left most of the combatants with vast stocks of almost indestructible weapons and even vaster stocks of ammunition to fire from them. While all this existed, no treasury official in his right mind would dare approve re-equipping with something radically new – and expensive – which would automatically transpose the stock piles into scrap piles. Germany, by virtue of the Versailles Treaty, was largely exempt from this drawback, but was, instead, provided with another and unique one – Adolf Hitler, who could almost be relied upon to ignore the sound and sensible suggestion of experts and plunge with reckless abandon after lunatic will-o-the-wisp schemes promising the military equivalent of get-rich-quick.

And speaking of lunatic schemes, I was cheered to find that some of the abortive ideas have found a place in these pages. It is salutary to look back at some of the ideas which didn't quite make it for one reason and another, if only for the insight they give us into the frame of mind and climate of thought which gave rise to them. Readers may scoff at the description of the three-man tank-burning team, but as an ex-member of one, I can assure them that we really did practice this suicidal antic in all seriousness. Indeed I can cap John Week's tale by pointing out another 'approved' technique of those years, one which actually achieved the status of recommendation in a training manual; one man with a hand grenade and a hammer was stationed at a first-floor window. As the enemy tank rolled past beneath, he leaped onto the turret and hammered on the hatch. When the enemy commander opened up to see what the devil all the noise was about, the hand grenade was pitched in by our intrepid hero, who then slammed the hatch shut and sat on it to contain the ensuing explosion. Ho! we were gay lads in those far-off days!

And it is in the reflected light of those days that one wants to read the following pages. The cold light of hindsight is no sort of illumination for examining the story of infantry weapons, for when the shooting is going on and the enemy is at the gates, many decisions have to be taken which can scarcely bear study in later and calmer years. Now the reader will see why some of those decisions were taken, rightly or wrongly, how they affected the soldier on the battlefield, and the consequences which followed from them. Over then, to John Weeks (M. Fusil, summa cum laude) as he unfolds before you the rich and variegated tapestry of Infantry Weapons of the Second World War.

# Sighting
# shots

The infantryman in the First World War learned a comparatively simple job. It may not have been a pleasant one, and for far too many it proved to be fatal, but by and large his knowledge of weapons had to extend to very little more than his rifle and bayonet, together with his shovel. With these tools he fought a war which was still very 19th Century in its outlook, and almost barbarically simple in the demands it made on him. The results were so appalling that in the years afterwards a good deal of effort was put into re-equipping the infantryman, and giving him even greater fire power and effectiveness. By 1939 the results of this effort were rather patchy, depending entirely on how much each country thought it could afford to spend, and how long each one had had to rearm. However, in the next five years the pace of change was dramatically fast, though, as always, it ultimately depended for its success entirely on the individual man in his trench or foxhole.

The soldier of the Second World War still had his rifle and bayonet, and he still had his shovel, but he now had to learn to handle a light machine gun as easily and competently as his rifle. He had to learn three or more grenades, a light mortar, and some sort of anti-tank weapon. As the war went on he had to master a sub-machine gun, more grenades, different anti-tank guns or projectors, and sometimes different rifles and machine guns. In three years' service he might have had to use as many as eight or nine different types of weapon, often more. If he was in any sort of special force such as a raiding party or paratroop, he might also have been taught the rudiments of the enemy's equipment so that he could use that if he had to without delay. He was still the same man who fought in Flanders in 1914, but he was becoming more of a weapon expert than his father ever dreamed of.

**Infantry go over the top armed only with rifles. The Somme, October 1916**

All this equipment was the weaponry of the infantry, and it did not matter what nationality the soldier was; the changes were pretty universal. Only in Russia, and, in a lesser respect, Japan also was the infantryman restricted to a few weapons or even one. These countries had special reasons for being so simple in their outlook; not the least of these was the somewhat sketchy training organisation, a huge army to train and equip, and little time in which to do it. One man, one gun was also attractive when the recruit came from a primitive agricultural background, but it was wasteful in the employment of that recruit, and restricted the tactical use of the formations that he joined. To the Soviets this was the least of their troubles, and the outstanding feature of their operations between 1941 and 1945 was the simplicity, one might almost say the crudity, of their battlefield tactics, which led to that extraordinary phenomenon of the war, the tank rider units, armed throughout with nothing heavier than sub-machine guns.

The whole range of infantry weapons is so broad that it is more than this book can hope to cover, for this reason a limit has had to be set on the scope, and it has been restricted to the commonest of all infantry fighting tools, the personal weapon or small arm. Even here the field is wide enough, starting at pistols and running up to medium machine guns, and it is this family which this book examines. There is no intention to give a history of small arms as it is assumed that the reader is sufficiently acquainted with the background to be able to understand how the Second World War equipments were developed. If there is any doubt on this rather specialist subject, there is a huge range of books on it, and the bibliography at the end of this one will provide all that is necessary for a good general knowledge. In particular, the small text book *Pistols, Rifles and Machine Guns* will be found to explain the most abstruse detail in simple and concise language, together with clear illustrations. Neither is there space within the confines of this book to examine the fascinating areas of infantry equipment made up by mortars, grenades, and particularly anti-tank weaponry.

In small arms, the Second World War not only speeded the development of existing weapons, but it also saw the introduction of several new ones. Chief among these introductions was one of general philisophy more than of any actual hardware. The main thread of this philosophy was the acceptance of quick and simple manufacturing techniques for small arms. Until the start of the war all weapons were made, with the exception of a tiny number just starting in Germany in 1938, by processes which involved many careful and accurate machining operations, the use of high quality materials, and careful and precise fitting of parts using skilled workmen. This is both slow and expensive, and as armies demand huge quantities of small arms,

it takes many factories and a tremendous organisation to meet the demand. Nazi Germany was the first to realise this, and, as will be seen in the later chapters, went to great lengths to modify small arms designs to allow for simpler manufacture, and cheaper metals. The result was that although the German war industry was badly bombed and disrupted, the small arms output was able to keep pace, just about, until the last few months of the war, when general chaos was setting in anyway. The tremendous advantage of designing for manufacture rather than for indefinite life in use was quickly seen by the Allies and copied, and so appeared such gunmakers' horrors as the sten gun and the M 3 'grease gun', both of which were perfectly effective and ideally cheap, though in the eyes of the specialist makers they were hideous almost beyond words. The high standards of military gunsmithing had come straight from the civilian contractors who made most of them

**Russian tank-riders, equipped with PPSh M 1941 sub-machine guns, about to accept the surrender of German infantry**

anyhow, and they applied their inherited techniques from the competitive civilian market.

The next was the rise of the sub-machine gun, which followed or accompanied the trend towards simplicity of manufacture. This weapon was the one which really brought personal firepower to the infantry battle, and in the early stages of the war the skilful use of it by the German army led to feelings of near panic among the more timid of the Allies. The sub-machine gun was the ideal complementary weapon for the high powered rifle of the Second World War. It offered rapid fire coupled with ease of handling and low weight, the only penalty being in range. It is incredible to think that in 1939 there must only have been a few thousand, perhaps 50,000 or 60,000 in existence, and five years later there

were 10,000,000, at a conservative estimate. The mind can hardly take in what these figures mean in factory effort, human endeavour, and sheer money and raw materials. And yet, after such a phenomenal birth, it now looks as though that same sub-machine gun is already becoming outdated and obsolete. Weapons have advanced so rapidly that the modern small calibre rifle can do the job of the sub-machine gun as well as a rifle, and in ten years there may well be no more in service in the first line armies of the world.

Another innovation during the war was the medium power cartridge, which is examined in the chapter dealing with the assault rifle. This was something which had long been realised as a need if there was to be any advance in rifle techniques, yet economic reasons had always held it back. It took the foresight of a small German team, helped by having a comparatively clean sheet from which to work, to produce what has become the commonplace type of military cartridge of our time: and from this the rifle which fires it. It is interesting to follow the history of these and other new ideas and see how often it was that the originals were the brain children of German designers. The engineering capability and invention of the German people has given much to the world, and prominent among these gifts has been the development of weapons of war. Not that conditions always favoured an inventor in Nazi Germany since policy was always subordinate to the organs of the political machine, and frequently required the approval of the Führer himself. Hitler's judgement was probably faulty, particularly when he tried to apply his own limited military experience to new and revolutionary ideas, and all too often it seems as if new weapons were introduced in spite of Hitler, rather

**Personal firepower is brought to the infantry battle through the use of sub-machine guns; MP 38/40**

than because of him. But this never stopped the steady flow of novelties, the only trouble for the Germans was that too many of these novelties were either not pursued to their ultimate conclusion, or that there was insufficient factory capacity to make them in significant numbers. And sometimes useful factory effort was diverted to unproductive weapons which should never have been started. Grenades for the signal pistol was a typical example.

Yet another innovation which was directly linked to simple manufacture was the principle of designing weapons so that they could be made in sub-components, or sections, which were made in different parts of the country, and assembled in one place to make the complete weapon. This was the first war in which such a technique had been necessary because no other war had been troubled by the long range strategic bomber with its steady, deliberate destruction of war effort. Thus it was that all manner of industries were pulled in to make parts for small arms, until it was literally true that shoe firms were making gun barrels and watch makers were making triggers. The sheer volume of production was immense, but the demand was equally so as the war dragged on into successive years, and the combatants mobilised larger and larger armies all demanding more and more arms and ammunition to continue the fight. In Britain the largest manufacturer of small arms in the early months of the war was the BSA company, but one night in 1941 the central factory was bombed and the huge barrel shop almost entirely destroyed. The response by the company was to decentralise to small firms all round the district, and almost every conceivable trade that had some sort of machine shop was arbitrarily taken over, gun-making machines from the main factory moved in within hours, and production started even before the former owners had had time to move themselves out. As soon as a

**Birmingham Small Arms factory after the bombing of 1941**

machine was set up, the power was connected and gun making began. As more machines arrived the process continued, and lorries carried raw materials and finished parts to and fro. The output was never again allowed to drop, but it demanded a tremendous effort, and was probably not very efficient in terms of manpower.

While this decentralisation seems now to be a logical and obvious thing to do, it did not appear so to many people at the time, who saw their life's work being thrown over without ceremony. There was hostility and opposition in many cases, but there was a form of financial compensation from the government which softened the blow to some extent, and there could be no arguing with the requisition officer. Of course, this sort of thing was not only confined to Britain; in Germany, too, small factories were taken over by the dozen and put on to weapon manufacture. One great advantage that small arms have over artillery pieces is that they are small, and the component parts can be easily handled by one man. With guns and carriages the factory floor has to have cranes and gantries to move the items being made, and the process cannot be subcontracted in anything like the same way as the hand guns. Much of the war-time small arms manufacture required simple tools like lathes, presses, and milling machines, all in the sort of sizes common to most light industry, and even roadside garages could be pressed into making components.

Ammunition could hardly be broken down in the same way to dozens of tiny centres, and for all the combatants the process of cartridge and bullet making was confined to a few highly automated factories. Cartridge cases require a series of deep drawing processes to make them, and this is something which is not common to any other industry, and requires special machinery if it is to be undertaken. It was certainly subcontracted to a few firms in Britain, who had in peace-time made roughly similar shaped containers, such as torch batteries, but even then they usually needed special cartridge machinery to be moved in. Filling the cartridges with propellant was entirely a function of the government factories, and could be undertaken otherwise only by firms who were in the ammunition trade in peace. It was essentially something which had to be done in proper surroundings, with special safety precautions, and for that reason and because their locations were well known such establishments were vulnerable to air attack. But a filling factory is a hard nut to crack with bombs, and there were several which were underground. Air raids had less effect on them than on other sources of weapon production.

Before launching the reader into further details of the small arms story of the Second World War, it would be as well briefly to outline what it is that is understood by the term, and then to show in the barest detail how these things work, since, without some knowledge of the interior workings of guns, much of the point of the discussions will be lost. This explanation will be sketchy in the extreme, but it should be enough for reasonable comprehension of what follows, and as has already been said, there is a host of specialised books which are only too eager to delve into the history and workings of the most intimate parts of every weapon ever made, but this is not one of them. A small arm is generally taken as being a bullet-firing weapon of less than 30mm calibre. For the purposes of this book the upper limit in calibre is about half an inch, or 13mm. Only by being so arbitrary and restrictive can the subject possibly be compressed into these covers, and the author must once more express his regret at being unable to look further at the other weapons which all properly belong to the infantry. Small arms are the weapons which are made and issued in the largest quantities to every man in the infantry as well as the other arms, and as the ones which are carried into the final assault and the hand to hand battle, they are, therefore, the most important in the armoury.

All small arms shoot a bullet of some sort, and in the Second World War the bullets which they shot were pretty well the same on both sides. The essentials of a round of small arms ammunition are a cartridge, the propellant powder, an igniter, and a bullet. The cartridge is placed in the open chamber at the breech end of a barrel, and the chamber closed by a breech block or bolt. A mechanical device strikes the igniter cap and starts the propellant burning. Within a thousandth or so of a second the propellant has all burned up into gas, and the pressure has risen to the order of several tons to the square inch. The bullet then starts to accelerate up the barrel, in fact it begins its movement before all the powder burns out, and rapidly reaches a very high speed indeed. On the way up it is spun to give it gyroscopic stability, and it then leaves the muzzle and flies towards its target. It is followed out of the barrel by a fast moving cloud of gas which is also hot and may be flaming. The ejection of this gas gives the characteristic explosion and muzzle flash, and some research has been put into devising means of reducing this for reasons of concealment. The empty cartridge case is left in the chamber, and has to be extracted and cleared away before a fresh round can be put in to repeat the process. This is the basis of all small arms firing; the mechanical process of lining up a round with the chamber, pushing it in, closing the breech, firing it, opening the breech, extracting the case, and finally throwing that case away. It presents a difficult problem to the designer to incorporate all these movements in one small compass, using the fewest possible parts, weighing as little as possible, with the least number of machining operations in their manufacture, using materials which are not urgently needed for other weapons, and finally being sturdy and reliable. Some did it superbly well, some did it miserably badly. To give an idea of what forces are involved, the pressure in the breech of the .30-inch US cartridge rose to twenty tons to the square inch for a period of just over one thousandth of a second, and the force pushing against the face of the bolt was fractionally under two tons! The period of time is so brief that the firer only feels a push of a few pounds as the impulse is spread out by the inertia of his rifle, but the face of the bolt is in no doubt about the magnitude of the force, and it needs to be made accordingly. Pistol rounds give far lower pressures and forces, but they are still in the region of tons, and are still remarkably dangerous.

In simple weapons, such as bolt action rifles, there is very little complication, but when the weapon is required to carry out all the firing cycle automatically, a whole host of ingenious mechanical devices come into play all of which employ the force of the explosion in some way to operate the mechanism. It is this mechanical miscellany that makes a study of small arms so fascinating. The basic power systems number three, with occasional mixtures of one with another, and the first one is recoil. This system has generally been applied to the heavier machine guns, but in the Second World War examples can be found throughout the whole range. Recoil is, of course, the most elementary force that is experienced by all who shoot a gun. In automatic weapons it is employed to move the barrel and bolt to the rear while the bullet travels up the bore. While they are still moving back the bolt is unlocked (the bullet having now gone), and the barrel is pushed forward by a spring. The backward moving bolt pulls out the empty case and, after ejecting it, pushes in another round while being forced forward by another spring. The illustration shows it quite clearly. It is the principle which is used in the Luger pistol among others. It has its own advantages and compensating drawbacks. Oddly enough, the amount of energy available is small, and is sometimes scarcely sufficient to work the mechanism, so that recoil boosters have to be employed, and the Vickers and the MG 42 are two good examples of boosted recoil guns. In these cases the booster is a chamber at the muzzle which traps some gas and allows it to expand and push the barrel back before being released. Another disadvantage is that the barrel has to move, and this is not easily accommodated in rifles and light machine guns, particularly as the latter usually need to have quick change barrels. On the credit side is the fact that it employs few working parts, imposes lower stresses on the mechanism and the general structure of the weapon, and is usually robust and reliable.

The next system is gas operation, in which the working force for the gun is supplied by tapping a small quantity of the propellant gas from the bore after the bullet has passed well up towards the muzzle, and so is not affected by any small pressure changes. This bit of gas is turned round in a vent or port, and directed backwards towards the breech, and is then allowed to flow down a cylinder and strike a piston. The piston is connected to the bolt and its locking latch, so that it first of all unlocks the bolt and then pushes it to the rear. A spring pushes it all forwards again to repeat the cycle. Gas operation is popular because it is generally light and not too complicated, and it can be varied in its action by altering the amount of gas taken from the barrel. Thus, if the gun is working in mud, or is fouled from long use and becoming

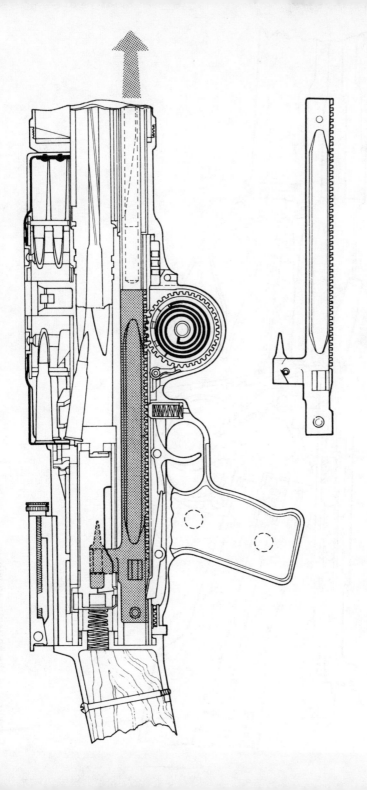

Cutaway drawing showing the gas operated piston of the .303 Lewis gun.

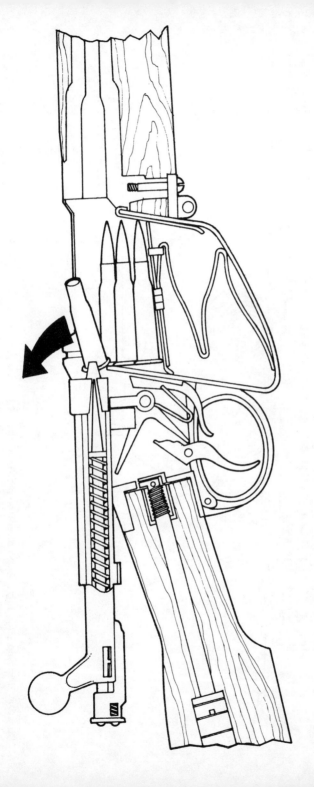

Cut away of the Enfield manually operated bolt action rifle

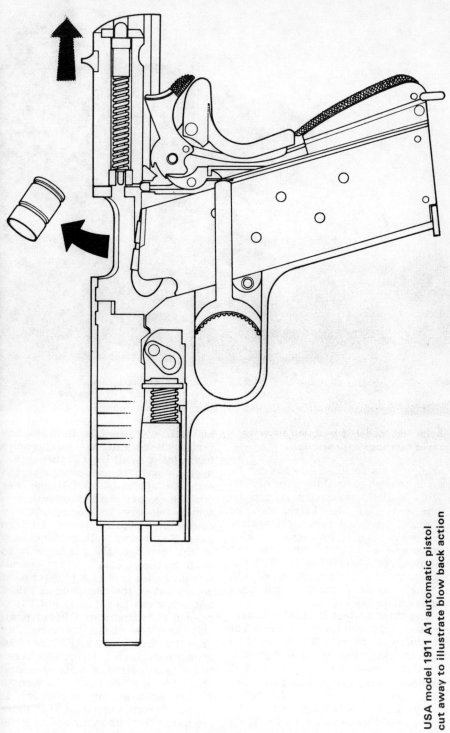

USA model 1911 A1 automatic pistol
cut away to illustrate blow back action

**8mm Fiat model 35 in action showing rapid cartridge case ejection**

sticky in its action, more gas can be let in to push everything a bit harder. With a little ingenuity it can be arranged that the barrel can be changed, and as a result the system has been popular for light machine guns and automatic rifles. In the Second World War it was probably the most widely used system of all, though in sheer numbers the next one perhaps beat it.

The third system is blowback, now quite widely used for all weapons, but in the Second World War confined to sub-machine guns and a few pistols, with the exception of a very small number of elderly machine guns used by the second line troops of the Italian army. In the blowback system the bolt is not locked to the barrel at all

and relies on inertia to keep the breech closed until the gas pressure has fallen to a safe level. It then moves back to open it and carry out the same sort of cycle as all the other ones do. The essence of the blowback system is a massive bolt, comparatively speaking, and a parallel sided cartridge case. The heavy bolt presents sufficient inertia to the gas pressure to keep the breech closed, and the parallel sided case acts as a plunger as it comes out of the chamber, and does not allow gas to get past until it is completely withdrawn. Of course, all this happens within an incredibly brief time frame; at a rate of fire of 600 rounds per minute each round is taken from its magazine or belt, fired, and ejected within one tenth of a second. If this tenth is split up further, it quickly becomes apparent that there are only a few hundredths of a second

during which the cartridge is in the chamber at all, the rest being taken up with movement. At the moment when the cap is struck in a blowback action, the bolt is still moving forward and it is brought to rest not by coming up against the face of the breech, but by being pushed back by the cartridge case under the gas pressure. In properly designed guns the bolt will never actually touch the breech face, but will move back a fraction of an inch before hitting it. All this calls for great care in the design, and equally great care in the manufacture of the ammunition, since, as can be seen, this sort of gun is most sensitive to changes in the power of the round, and also to dirt on the surfaces that the bolt rides on. However, it is simple, remarkably so, and it has been used in pistols for many years. It was brought to real prominence in the Second World War with sub-machine guns, all of which used blowback in one form or another, and all of which fired from an open bolt. It will be seen that if the bolt is allowed to close on a cartridge, then the inertia is lost, and the recoil of the bolt will be very violent, so it is always arranged therefore that the gun stops firing with the bolt held to the rear. The first shot takes an appreciable time from when the trigger is pulled to when the round goes off. During this time the heavy bolt flies forward, feeding in a round, and generally disturbing the firer's aim. There is nothing that can be done to prevent this, and it is a feature of all the successful military designs. After this first shot the movement of the gun naturally becomes even more violent, and few sub-machine guns can be held on to one aiming mark while firing automatic.

# Pistols

No other weapon attracts the imagination so much as a pistol. It is small, compact, ingenious, generally well made, and possessed of a mystique all its own. It is famed in legend and song, it is deadly, and finally, it is available.

Military pistols are often so similar to the civil model as to be indistinguishable, though this is not always the case. A few are readily recognized as being made specially for service use, and then the differences are obvious. Literally hundreds of different pistols have been made and used in the world, and many of them were probably carried and no doubt used, during the Second World War. As it would be quite impossible to describe more than a small number, this chapter will confine itself to those which were officially adopted for service in the chief countries concerned, and this study in itself covers such a wide field that it has been found necessary to cut out several individual models which it is known were used by one or another combatant. Even in this brief survey the range of calibres covers .32-inches to .455-inches, and it is known for sure that the spectrum could be extended to .22-inches at the lower end, so letting in an infinity of hand guns.

The traditional use of the military pistol is to provide personal defence of men armed with weapons other than rifles, and on its own the pistol is relatively unimportant when compared with other small arms. By repute it is rarely used in battle, and

one prominent general known to the author has said that in the Second World War he was present when precisely thirty men were killed or wounded by pistol fire. Sadly, twenty-nine were of his own side, and were the victims of accidental discharges, or neglect of safety precautions. The odd one was an enemy whom the general himself shot, but found that this was not conclusive and he had to be finished off with a sub-machine gun. This is no way to advertise pistols, but it could just be that it is a fair estimate of their military value. In the hands of the average soldier the standard of marksmanship is poor, although the weapon and its ammunition is intrinsically accurate. In the hands of an inexperienced or enthusiastic soldier a pistol roughly equates in safety to a grenade with the pin removed. Its small size makes it remarkably handy for quick use, and equally remarkably dangerous. Proper use of a pistol can save a

Chinese guerrillas armed with (left) a Mauser 39K, (centre) a Browning automatic pistol and (right) a Mauser automatic of 7.63mm or .45 calibre

soldier's life, improper use can prematurely end a friend's life, and it frequently has done so. The difficulty with pistols is that continuous practice and careful training are vital to their safe and effective use. In wartime few armies have the time for either.

But so much for the philosophy, now to the facts. Pistols come in two forms as most readers will know, revolvers and automatics. Argument about the merits of each has raged for over fifty years, but it is now accepted that automatics are the better, and nearly all nations use them. During the Second World War the dichotomy had by no means been resolved, and both types were found in all armies. Revolvers are generally simpler, safer, and stronger. Furthermore it is easy to see if they are loaded or not, and this is popular with soldiers. Automatics, or self loading pistols to give them their correct name, are generally lighter, carry more ammunition, and fire faster. But after each shot the breech is reloaded, and the action is cocked onto a fresh round. Both types are handy in confined spaces, but have a short effective range. On the subject of range, lest any reader should be so ill advised as to take the Western films at their face value, the lethal range of the heaviest pistol round is about 300 yards – assuming that the victim is hit in a vital spot, such as the middle of the head. For others it is much closer, but as there are very few pistol users who can hit a barn door at much more than ten paces (or as one colourful character put it, can scarcely hit the ocean from a dinghy), the matter of range only embraces the laws of accident and chance. It is something which is dealt with at length in the specialist books.

Prewar, the British preference was

firmly for revolvers, and the standard side arm of the British army from 1936 until 1957 was the Enfield .38-inch Revolver Number 2 Mark 1. This was a simple pistol taken from a Webley and Scott design of the early 1920s modified in the lock mechanism to some extent by the Royal Small Arms Factory at Enfield, and chambered for a new and more powerful cartridge developed at the same factory. It was ordinary in every way, its two main characteristics being remarkable reliability and equally remarkable inaccuracy in the hands of the average user. Enfield's work on the trigger action resulted in stiffness in use, and a terrifying pull off when firing double action. This could be modified with an oil stone and some skill so that the pistol could be fired quite sweetly and accurately, but the only people interested in doing this sort of thing were the target shooters, and the wartime models were left much as they were made. A variation of the design, called the Mark 1* had the comb of the hammer removed so that vehicle crews and others who worked in confined spaces would not suffer the annoyance of their pistol catching on projections as they moved about. The result was a pistol which it was almost impossible to hold steady when shooting without the wrist muscles of a Hercules. The useful range of this particular model is little more than point blank, at which it excels as it never jams and a misfire merely delays the next shot. This fact is another important difference between the two types of pistol. A misfire in an automatic pistol requires the slide to be pulled back by the free hand to clear the dud round and feed another, by which time the firer may well be dead. The revolver shooter just keeps on pulling the trigger, and it makes no difference to the mechanism whether the hammer falls on a dud round or a live one.

It would be an exaggeration to say that the Enfield was popular. It was tolerated and that was about all. Whenever an opportunity offered

**Enfield pistol Number 2 Mk I;** *Calibre:* **.38;** *System of Operation:* **Single or double action;** *Length:* **10.25 inches;** *Barrel Length:* **5 inches;** *Feed Device:* **Cylinder, 6 chambers;** *Front Sights:* **Blade;** *Rear Sights:* **Square notch;** *Weight:* **1.58 lbs;** *Muzzle Velocity:* **600 feet per second**

other pistols were 'liberated' or purloined, and the Enfield discarded. Italian Berettas and German P 38s were favourites, though really anything was preferred. Another revolver in British service was the .38-inch Smith and Wesson, which was bought in large numbers from the USA. This was a much better proposition than the Enfield, being easier to hold and shoot, and having a delightful trigger which helped for quite accurate shooting. The light trigger controlled a hammer that was also rather light in its strike, and often gave too gentle a blow to fire the wartime ammunition, so that a few modifications were required to the main spring.

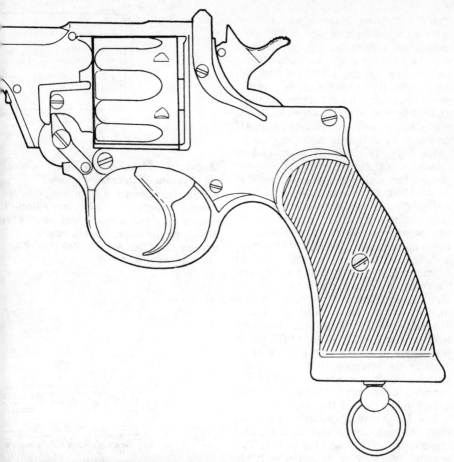

An officer takes sight from behind cover with his .38 Enfield 'pistol'

The Smith and Wesson was not as strong as the Enfield and really hard use could loosen all its joints and make its action even more uncertain, but it was sought after by the discerning soldier. Finally, there was one automatic pistol in British service, and this was the Browning 9mm, made in Canada and issued in small numbers to airborne and commando units only. It has stayed on and is now the standard pistol, having replaced the Enfield entirely. There is little that is remarkable about it except for the fact that the magazine holds thirteen rounds, and is one of the biggest made for any pistol. It holds the ammunition in a double row, and the butt which surrounds it is comfortably wide to hold as a result. The early models had a tangent backsight scaled up to 500 yards and a slot on the butt to fit on a stock. These stocks were never issued, and any soldier who tried to shoot at 500 yards was achieving very little more than raising his own morale. It was highly popular with its users and has remained unchanged throughout the thirty-five years of its existence.

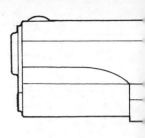

**Model 1911 A1 Automatic Pistol;** *Calibre* **.45;** *System of Operation:* **Recoil Automatic;** *Length:* **8.62 inches;** *Barrel Length:* **5 inches;** *Feed Device:* **7 Round, in-line, detachable box magazine;** *Sights Front:* **Blade; *Rear:* Square notch; *Weight:* 2.43 lbs; *Muzzle Velocity:* 830 feet per second**

The US Army standardized on the Colt .45-inch automatic in 1911, and the gun is still in service today. The Second World War model was little different from the original, and it was used by all arms and services in the US Army throughout the world. There were just about sufficient stocks to initiate this vast deployment because many thousands remained from the First World War, and manufacture had not ceased during peace time. In fact, there were enough to allow Britain to buy some thousands during 1940, and manufacture restarted promptly after Pearl Harbor, to equip the expanding US forces. Tremendous affection has been generated by the Colt, and it is undoubtedly a very sound and reliable design. It originated in a pistol produced by Browning in 1897, which Colt manufactured and progressively improved until arriving at the 1911 model. The pistol is immensely robust, simple

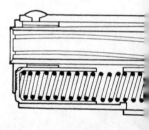

**Cut away of a USA M 1911 A1 automatic pistol**

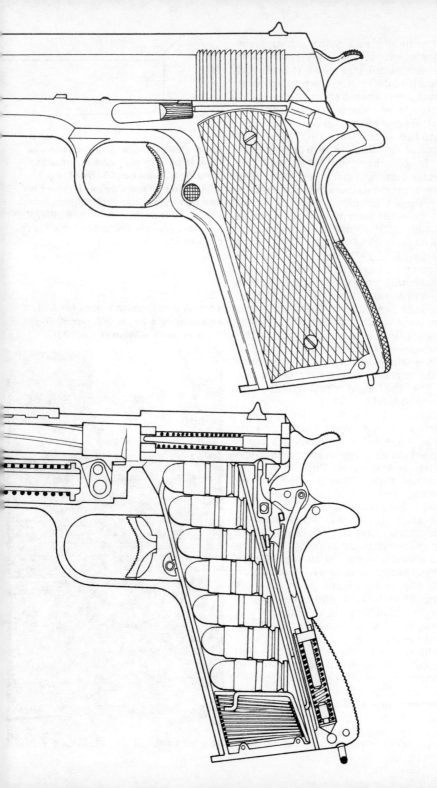

and reliable; and many small arms experts rate it as being the best military pistol ever made. It is always difficult to determine the best or worst in weapons because there are so many factors to be considered that the final analysis has to rely on opinion rather than tabulated facts, but since the Colt has remained in military service for longer than any other, and has survived two world wars with only very minor modification, it can be no ordinary pistol.

It fires the enormous bullet of the .45-inch ACP round, a round which was adopted after the Philippine Campaign of 1900, when .38-inch was found to be too light to stop charging tribesman. The Colt bullet weighs one-third more than the bullet the standard NATO rifle fires, and this enormous weight has to have a heavy pistol if the recoil is not to break the firer's wrist. There is no doubt that the Colt is pocket artillery in every sense of the expression, but despite its size it fits the hand comfortably and shoots straight.

Despite the large stocks of Colts, there were not quite enough to go round to all US troops, and some carried .45-inch revolvers, mainly the Smith and Wesson. This was a big brother of the .38-inch used by the British, and differed little from it except that it fired a rimless cartridge, and had an ingenious clip system to support and eject it. For the most part the revolvers went to military police and service troops, with the Marine Corps taking some. Apart from these few, the story of pistols in the US Army of 1941-45 is simply the story of the Colt, and there is no question but that the US Army was lucky to have a good model.

The German army entered the war armed with a pistol which was to become the most popular and prized souvenir of the whole war – outshining even the Japanese officers' swords – this was the Luger 9mm Model 08. There are probably more misconceptions about this weapon than any

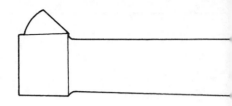

Luger P08; *Calibre:* 9mm; *System of Operation:* Recoil, semi-automatic; *Length:* 8.75 inches; *Barrel Length:* 4.06 inches; *Feed Device:* 8 round in-line box magazine; *Front Sights:* Blade; *Rear Sights:* 'V' notch; *Weight:* 1.93 lbs; *Muzzle Velocity:* 1,050 feet per second

*Left:* A soldier with tripod for MG 34 and holding a Luger P08 pistol. *Right:* SS man with a Mauser KAR 98K

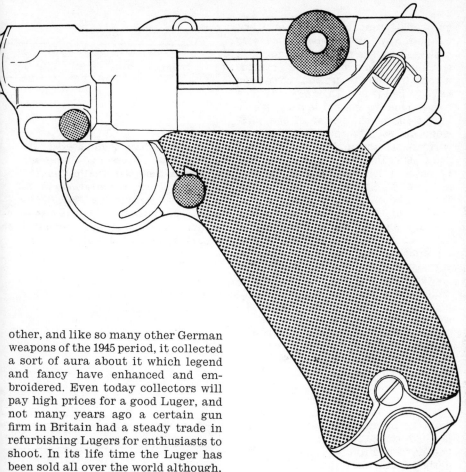

other, and like so many other German weapons of the 1945 period, it collected a sort of aura about it which legend and fancy have enhanced and embroidered. Even today collectors will pay high prices for a good Luger, and not many years ago a certain gun firm in Britain had a steady trade in refurbishing Lugers for enthusiasts to shoot. In its life time the Luger has been sold all over the world although, apart from Germany, it was only officially adopted as a service weapon in the smaller countries of the world, among them those in South America. No large army took it. Incredibly, even Vickers of Britain made some. This was one order for 10,000 for the Netherlands government in the 1920s, though why the Dutch did not try to buy ex-First World War stocks is hard to see.

The Luger was adopted in the German army in 1908 (hence the Model 08), and 2,000,000 were made between 1914 and 1918. Most of these seem to have been removed after the Armistice, so that when Nazi Germany came to rearm in the early 1930s there were few left and produc-

tion had to start again. By 1938 it had become increasingly expensive to manufacture, and the simpler P 38 was adopted as a replacement. Production was ordered to halt, but it continued until 1942 as the army generally preferred the Luger and wanted to carry it, so another 400,000 were made, bringing the grand total of all manufactured to 3,000,000. In some respects at least, prewar Germany was not quite the rigid dictatorship that we are sometimes given to believe. As a pistol the Luger is not as good as its reputation. It is certainly elegant, it handles well and it will shoot accurately and pleasantly, but it suffers a

29

number of limitations for a military weapon. First of all it is expensive to make. There are many small parts in the mechanism which require careful machining and fitting, and the springs have to be made with some care. The toggle locking system is sensitive to variations in the power of the cartridge, and too little or too much power will jam the action. Mud, dirt, ice and snow also cause jams, and, as there is no cover on the mechanism, there is nothing to stop them getting in. When put alongside the P 38 there is no doubt which is the better military pistol, which makes the decision to continue manufacture of the Luger for another four years all the more surprising. In the First World War there were several additional bits which could be fitted to the standard pistol, the most common being the wooden shoulder stock to make a small carbine, but this was rarely seen in the 1939 war although the lug for it remained on the butt. Oddities such as the huge 32-round 'snail' magazine, and tangent backsights reading to 800 metres died in 1918.

Another veteran which survived from the distant past and whose manufacture started again in the 1930s was the Mauser military pistol which was designed and first produced in 1895. It is big, awkward, ungainly, expensive to make, and not suited to mass production. Having said all that, it is pleasant to fire and quite accurate. Production started again in 1932 after a fourteen-year gap, probably for the very good reason that no other design was available at the time and, as a result, several thousand were made until production finally stopped in 1945, though the grand total for the fifty years of the Mauser's life is only about a million, which is not large for a small arm. This pistol was frequently used as a carbine by fitting a wooden stock and one version was fully automatic and intended to be a light machine pistol. It was originally issued to service and echelon troops, but in the chaos of 1945 and the last

**Mauser Automatic Pistol Model 1916;** *Calibre:* 9mm; *System of Operation:* Blowback, Semi-Automatic; *Length Overall:* 6.2 inches; *Barrel Length:* 3.4 inches; *Weight:* 1.31 lbs; *Feed Device:* 8 Round, in-line detachable box magazine; *Sights: Front:* Blade; *Rear:* Round notch *Muzzle Velocity:* 950 feet per second

**Cross section of the Mauser automatic pistol 1916 showing the unusual magazine position**

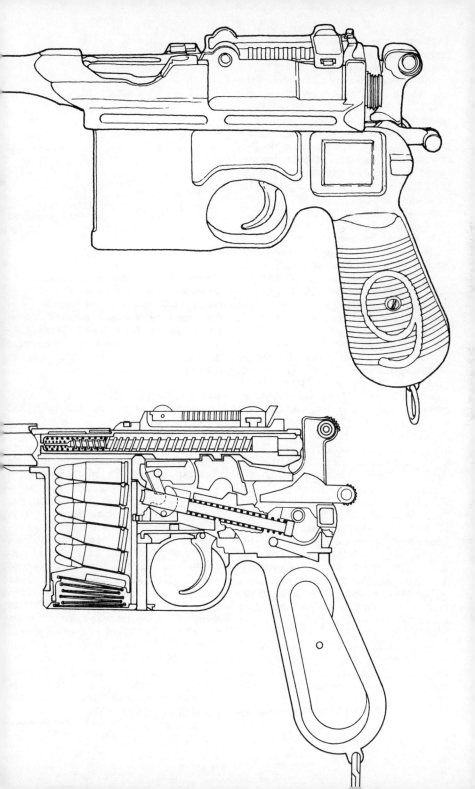

days of the war any weapon was pressed into use and the Mauser was frequently used by the infantry.

The standard German pistol, and the one which finally replaced the Luger was the Walther P 38, which is still manufactured in Germany, and again in service in the German army. It is a straightforward automatic pistol of conventional design except for its novel double action trigger. When the pistol is loaded it can be carried with a round in the chamber and the hammer down. It is then quite safe. To fire, the trigger is pulled and it then cocks the hammer, releasing it at full cock to strike the cartridge. Recoil then recocks for another and subsequent shots. The P 38 was the first military pistol to have this double pull, and it is an innovation of some value; at the same time there is another and separate safety lever which locks the firing pin. Despite all this apparent complication the mechanism is simple and straightforward, and manufacture is relatively easy. One would expect that it might become in due time a rival of the Colt as the best military pistol ever made. It was issued on a wide scale in the Wehrmacht, who were generally more pistol conscious than the Allies. At first the Luger was preferred by the officers and the P 38 given to the enlisted men, but by 1944 its use was quite general throughout all ranks. It performs well in dirt and dust, though some models from 1944 onwards were made from defective materials, which wore out quickly, and their mechanisms became unsafe. Altogether, about one million P 38s were made during the war years, in three separate factories, of which Walther was only one.

There is one other German pistol which deserves a brief mention, and that is the signal pistol, or *Kampfpistole* as it was termed. All signal pistols are pretty well similar in that they are single shot weapons of reasonably large calibre which fire a pyrotechnic projectile at a low velocity to

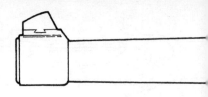

Walther P38; *Calibre:* 9mm; *System of Operation:* Recoil, semi-automatic; *Length:* 8.6 inches; *Barrel Length:* 4.9 inches; *Feed Device:* 8 round in-line box magazine; *Front Sights:* blade; *Rear Sights:* Rounded notch; *Weight:* 2.1 lbs; *Muzzle Velocity:* 1,115 feet per second

a maximum range of about sixty yards. There is nothing particularly lethal about them unless one is unlucky enough to get in the way of the burning projectile while it is still travelling fast near to the muzzle. But the Germans turned this simple pistol into a grenade projector by making a small cylindrical explosive round for it, and giving it rifling for stability. The calibre was 27mm, and the grenade weighed just over five ounces with its propellant, of which three-and-a-half ounces travelled to the target. Not surprisingly, no great damage accompanied the arrival of such a modest shell, particularly as some of the weight was taken up with a neat fuze. In flight it made a wobbling low whistle as it traversed the thirty odd yards to its target, and gave sufficient time for an alert man simply to duck his head. It was an ingenious idea, and sensible from one point of view in that it gave the signal pistol another, and more warlike role. Unfortunately, such tiny grenades

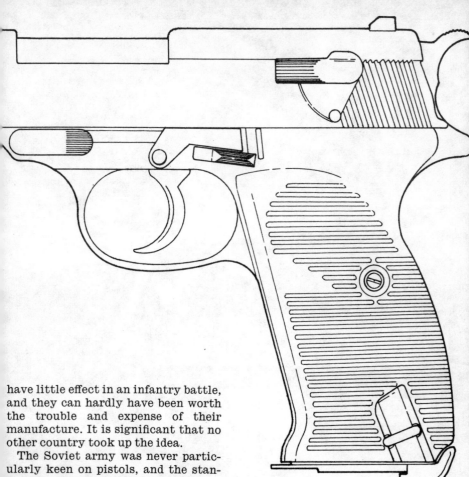

have little effect in an infantry battle, and they can hardly have been worth the trouble and expense of their manufacture. It is significant that no other country took up the idea.

The Soviet army was never particularly keen on pistols, and the standard Second World War weapon was a slightly simplified version of the 1911 Browning, rechambered for 7.63mm Mauser ammunition. Soviet Russia had large stocks of this round when the pistol was designed in the late 1920s and it made sense to use it. Named the Tokarev after its designer, the pistol was made in quite large quantities in the various Soviet arsenals, with a varying degree of finish and sophistication. The advent of the sub-machine gun all but finished off pistols as a weapon in Russia except for vehicle crews and some service troops and staff officers. The Russian philosophy was more inclined towards offensive rather than defensive weaponry, and the pistol did not fit the bill. For all that, the Tokarev

was a robust and effective weapon, and apparently worked extremely well in poor conditions and with little attention. It has been made under licence in most of the Eastern Bloc countries since the war, and still survives in service.

The Japanese, on the other hand, stuck to pistols because they never developed a sub-machine gun to rival them. In any case they were to a great extent traditional in their equipment, and officers carried swords and pistols as their standard weapons. The one that they had was, like so many Japanese weapons, rather odd looking to Western eyes. It was the 8mm Type 14 Nambu, produced in 1925 as a

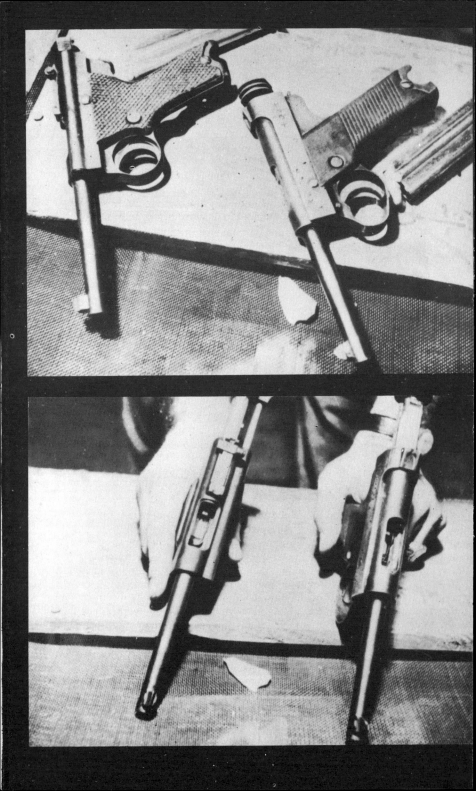

modification to a 1914 Nambu which it closely resembled. The general outline is not unlike a Luger, though there is no other resemblance. The mechanism is quite different, and the standard of manufacture is generally poor. It was apparently adequately serviceable, though the models which remain today look as though not enough attention was given to detailed items such as small springs and pins, and jams and breakages may have been more frequent than with other designs. The Type 14 was backed up by the Type 11, a 1934 model. If the Type 14 was a doubtful design, the Type 11 was quite simply bad. It is a recoil operated automatic with an oddly squat look, occasioned by a lack of proportion in the receiver and butt. The trigger mechanism can be made to fire before the bolt has closed onto the breech, and another hazard is the fact that the trigger sear runs along the outside of the receiver, and can be operated either by dropping onto the ground, or simply by careless handling. As can be seen, the Type 11 is by no means an ideal weapon, and why it was ever accepted for the Japanese military is a complete mystery. In 1934 there were plenty of good weapons to choose from in Europe and the USA, and one can only suppose that patriotism was paramount. Like the Nambu, it fired the weak 8mm round, peculiar to the Japanese.

The final pistol which we will consider is the Italian Beretta and, unlike some other infantry weapons

made in Italy before the war, the Beretta was quite first class. It was well made, sensibly designed, and adequately effective. Originally produced in 1915, it was progressively improved until the model of 1934, which is the one that was used throughout the Second World War. It is once more being made in Italy, and is still very little altered from the design of nearly forty years ago. The Beretta was much sought after as a souvenir by Allied troops in the African and Italian campaigns, and many thousands travelled homewards with GIs and Tommies to be kept as mementoes or used for self defence. It is a small blowback operated automatic pistol which fits easily into a pocket, though the issue models had holsters. It has a short barrel only three-and-a-half inches long, and is only six inches overall. It is snub nosed, and a bit small in the butt, so that the hand overlaps and a spur projects from the magazine floor for the firer's little finger to rest on. Like any other weapon made by Beretta, the finish and general standard of manufacture is extremely high, and this was maintained until the Italian surrender in 1943 when the factory was taken over by the occupying German forces and from then on the quality declined gradually. The calibre is 9mm, but the round was the 9mm short, or .380 auto cartridge, which is a different proposition from the more common Parabellum, and the latter is too powerful for it. There was also a 7.65mm (.32-inch) version.

The Beretta was standard issue throughout the Italian army until replaced in 1952, and was also given to partisans and guerilla forces. It was reliable, strong, and satisfactory in every way, despite the fact that it looks much more like a civilian weapon than one made specially for the military. The short barrel limited the effective range to little more than twenty or thirty yards but this is adequate for all normal actions, and the Italian army made no complaints.

*Top and bottom left:* 8mm Nambu model automatic pistol, 8 rounds in the magazine. *Top and bottom right:* 8mm Taisho model 14 1925 automatic. The general outline of these weapons is similar to a Luger, though there is no other resemblance. The mechanism is quite different, and the manufacture was generally poor. There were plenty of good weapons to choose from in Europe and the USA, so one can only suppose that the Japanese chose on patriotic grounds

# Sub-machine guns

Every war has its special weapon, by which is meant the one which came to notice in that war alone, and which every combatant had to have in his armoury in order to compete with his adversaries. In the American Civil War it was the breech loading rifle in its many complicated forms. In the First World War it was the aeroplane, the submarine, and the machine gun.

The Second World War saw the birth of several weapons, not least being the atomic bomb which obviously outstrips all others in importance, but in the more mundane field of infantry fighting the greatest radical introduction was the sub-machine gun. It is probably not too much to say that it ranks nearly as high in importance as the innovation of the auto

matic principle itself. Like so many weapons of the past, the sub-machine gun was not new when the war started. The story, in fact, goes back to the First World War, the first to be used being the Italian Villar Perosa. These little guns were surprisingly similar to the ones which we all know today, but the earlier models were mounted in pairs and used rather more as light machine guns. It is hardly surprising that they were unsuccessful in this role, but tactical sense prevailed and by the end of the war the Italian army evolved a more satisfactory way of

A Yugoslav partisan armed with a 9mm M 34 Steyr Solothurn sub-machine gun. Also known as the MP 34(0), it was used by the German police

employing their new weapon. It was carried by one man and employed as mobile fire support for assaulting troops in the slow, ponderous infantry attacks which were such a feature of the First World War, and for the smaller actions in which the Italian army engaged in the mountains along its northern borders. However, for some reason they failed to use it as it

**A German soldier uses a Bergman MP 18 during the height of the Russian winter**

is used now, perhaps because of the designer's fixation with bipod mountings, and the lack of a shoulder stock. These shortcomings were put right in the immediate successor to the Villar Perosa, which was a modification to the original gun involving a wooden stock, and made by Beretta, a name which recurs with increasing frequency from then on.

The Beretta model was actually in service in 1918, and continued with the Italian infantry until 1940. It can probably be taken as the originator of all the sub-machine guns of the world, although the German MP 18 has almost equally strong claims to the same distinction. MP 18 was designed by Hugo Schmeisser in the Bergmann factory in 1916. The production model appeared in the hands of troops in the summer of 1918 and just over 35,000 were made before the war ended. The

German army intended to train all officers, non-commissioned officers and ten per cent of every rifle company in the use of the weapon, and each company was to have a squad with six machine gunners and six ammunition carriers in it. None of this took place, but it is interesting to reflect on the tactical mentality which allocated a second man to the sub-machine gun, making it a two-man team, and to contrast this with the more realistic Italian approach. In fact the German intentions went further as it was also proposed to have a small ammunition cart for every two gun teams. Another eighteen years were to pass before the Wehrmacht came to realise the full potential of the sub-machine gun, but they were not alone in this failing; practically every other nation was similarly myopic. For us today, armed with the splendid historical power of hindsight it is difficult to see how such a revolutionary device could be overlooked, or how such few examples as did reach service could be so ineptly employed. There was no lack of invention of small handy weapons for trench raids and close infighting, but this one never seems to have been given a chance.

The authors of the Treaty of Versailles were sufficiently perceptive to prohibit the use of sub-machine guns by the German peace-time army, but among those armies who were free to take it up, few chose to do so. Apart from a small number of manufacturers, some police forces, a few naval and marine units, and a very limited number of armies, the sub-machine gun dropped into military obscurity. The next combat use came in the Gran Chaco War of 1932 where both sides in this jungle campaign used them, and bought as many as they could. No great notice appears to have been taken from this lesson, but within four years the clangour of another war rammed the teaching home once and for all. The Spanish Civil War saw the use of sub-machine guns in reasonable numbers for the first time and the German, Italian and Russian participators were not slow to grasp the point. All three set about designing and mass producing sub-machine guns in their own countries and had them in the hands of their troops before the approaching war began. Others, among them the USA and Britain, were less sensible.

The memorable feature of the Spanish war was that the tactical use of the sub-machine gun was at last realised. Gone were the ammunition carts and two-man teams, gone also were the light bipods and similar impedimenta. The guns were used by one man each time, and were employed to give greater firepower to the individual infantryman without affecting his mobility, which is the classic use of the sub-machine gun. At the same time there began the idea, although it was not to come to fruition for another seven years, that the weapon need not necessarily be expensive and carefully made. A lower standard of manufacture and finish

could be tolerated without danger to the firer or detriment to the performance, but quite naturally the traditional manufacturers were slow to take up this approach, and it needed the spur of war to convince them. Some of the German weapons of 1945 were unbelievably crude by prewar standards, yet they worked quite well for a short time, and that was all that was asked of them.

The story has now led us to 1938 and 1939, and at this point it will be as well to pause in the straight historical survey and examine the weapon which has emerged, and which set the pattern for all subsequent types and nationalities. The first significant feature of all sub-machine guns is the ammunition. In this sphere there has been almost complete, if inadvertent, standardisation between nations. A very light man-portable machine gun cannot possibly fire the same round as a rifle since the recoil would be far too great, and the power of the ammunition would shake the gun to pieces. From the very beginning pistol ammunition was selected as being adequate for the task, with the result that all the early models were made in 9mm, 7.65mm or, in the USA, .45-inch. This similarity is all the more interesting when it is realised that at this time there were almost as many rifle calibres as there were nations, and the same dissimilarity existed in artillery ammunition. Nevertheless it had the useful feature that one could use one's ally's or one's adversary's ammunition without trouble; though it seems that this was not a deliberate feature of any design until the British Sten of 1941. Pistol ammunition has an effective range of about 200 yards at the most, when fired from a barrel of 8 or 9 inches long; and accuracy begins to drop off above 100 yards. So the best ranges for its use are below 150 yards. For street fighting and similar close-quarter work this is more than enough, and it will usually encompass most infantry fighting on the open battlefield. Despite these

obvious facts, and it must be remembered that the ballistic performance of pistol ammunition was well known long before sub-machine guns came on the scene, several of the early designers fitted complicated and expensive sights to their weapons in which the maximum range was frequently as high as 1,000 yards or even more. It is true that a pistol bullet will travel this far, but it will be moving quite slowly when it does finally get there, and will do very little damage. These long range sights are a symptom of the current confusion of thought at the time that the weapons were produced, when designers were still thinking in terms of hand held light machine guns. From 1941 onwards all sub-machine guns were given a simple short range sight, often with no means of adjustment, and better suited to their proper task.

As has been said, pistol ammunition is relatively low powered, and it always features a straight sided cartridge case. This is important since the sub-machine gun action will not work with any other kind. All the 1939 sub-machine guns operated on the blow-back principle in its simplified form. The sequence has already been explained, but there are, of course, many variations to this simple cycle. The first is that the gun always fires from an open bolt, in other words the bolt is at the rear when the trigger is pulled. This means that there is a delay while the bolt moves forward, and also some slight movement of the weapon due to the push being exerted by the spring. Neither of these facts helps towards accurate shooting of the first round, and when firing automatic almost all sub-machine guns tend to push their barrels up into the air because of the rapid bolt movement and muzzle recoil. This spreads the shots even further abroad. The rate of fire depends upon a combina-

**American armed with a Thompson sub-machine gun advance against a pill box**

*Above:* A British soldier uses the very popular
German MP 38/40  *Below:* US Marines with Thompson
sub-machine guns in action on Okinawa

*Above:* Russian troops firing at the enemy east of Velikie Luki using PPSh M 1941 sub-machine guns. *Below:* A Thompson, this Philippino guerrilla's weapon

tion of bolt weight, return spring power, and ammunition design, but all nations arrived at a figure in the region of 600 rounds per minute. A higher rate meant that the firer could let off a whole magazine with one trigger pull and wasted most of the shots, a lower rate that he had fired too slowly for a fleeting target and might not have put enough bullets in the area to hit it. Not all designers agreed with this last point, and there are exceptions. Finally, all nationalities quickly came to use two types of magazine, though these were rarely interchangeable. The first was the simple box, which held twenty to thirty rounds, and the second was the round drum, holding fifty or more.

The general shape of the weapons came in all varieties, from ones which were hardly distinguishable from a standard rifle, and just about as heavy, to quite modern-looking all-metal designs with folding butts and folding magazines, weighing below 8 lbs.

The Italian army had been equipped with some sub-machine guns since the First World War, and so were really the leaders in the use and design of the species. However, they had let their lead slip a little until it was regained in 1938 with the Beretta model. This has been described by some authorities as the finest sub-machine gun ever made, and it continued in production in Italy until 1944. Many hundreds of thousands were made and were supplied to the German and Rumanian armies as well as equipping all the Italian forces. It is worth describing it in some detail because it represents what might be called the 'Old School' of thought on design, and it set the pattern for many similar weapons.

The Beretta was similar in outline to a short rifle. A one-piece wooden stock was cut into a fairly conventional shape with a long tubular receiver and barrel on the top surface. Overall length was just over three feet, a rifle type bayonet was fitted as standard, and the weight without

magazine was 9½ lbs. Magazines came in four sizes, 10, 20, 30 and 40 rounds in each. The sights were very similar to existing rifle sights, and the backsight was graduated in steps of 100 metres up to 500 metres. This seems highly optimistic in view of the known performance of its 9mm ammunition, but a special high velocity round was developed for this gun, which may have come near to realising the hopes of the sights. Two triggers were fitted, the forward one for automatic fire, and the rear one for single shots. A bolt handle projected on the right hand side, and finger grooves were cut into the sides of the stock. It was robust, fairly simple, heavy, and, above all, beautifully made.

The Beretta is, in fact, a shining example of the gun maker's art and it accurately reflects the views of the designers and military procurers who produced it. To them guns were made to last, and furthermore, were made by tried and proved processes using well known materials. Most of the metal parts of the Beretta were made of high quality steel machined out of the solid by expensive and slow methods. The only concession to mass production which occurred in the six years of manufacture was a sheet steel stamped jacket for the barrel. The resulting gun was excellent in every way, and is still in use today in some parts of the world, but it was out of date by the time it came into service. Later on in the war it was seen that the model 38 was too heavy and expensive and a simpler and lighter gun was produced. This was the model 38/42, with a short wooden stock, shorter barrel, fewer working parts, and little machining in the manufacture, most parts being made from steel stampings or welded components. Once again, both the German and Rumanian armies took delivery of some of the output, and they may well have influenced the design as well.

The model 38 Beretta continued in production for many years after the war ended, the last actual wartime

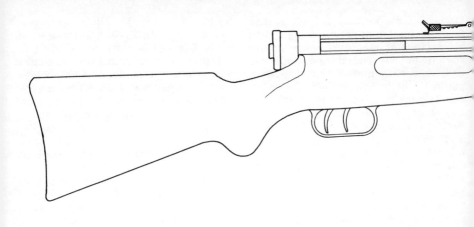

**Beretta Model 1938/42 Sub-Machine Gun (Early Model);** *Calibre:* 9mm Parabellum; *System of Operation:* Blowback, selective fire; *Length:* 31.5 inches; *Barrel Length:* 8.4 inches; *Feed Device:* 20- or 40-Round detachable staggered row, box magazine; *Sights: Front:* Blade: *Rear:* 'L' Type Flip over with U notch; *Weight:* 7.2 lbs; *Cyclic Rate:* 550 rounds per minute; *Muzzle Velocity:* 1,250 feet per second

version being the 38/44, which probably never saw service before the fighting finished. The peacetime Berettas were all similar in outline and general design to the original of 1938, though the process of simplification in manufacture was continued.

The German army had, to some extent, evaded the conditions of the Versailles Treaty by arming the police with the early Schmeisser designed sub-machine gun, and later on with the Bergmann. At the same time these factories were encouraged to manufacture outside Germany, and Bergmann for instance contracted his design and research to Denmark. The Schmeisser designed MP 28 was built in Belgium and Spain as well as in small quantities in Germany.

The fillip given to the sub-machine gun by the Spanish Civil War resulted in the German army finding itself armed with a variety of types in the opening months of 1939. As with most of their other military small arms, demand had outstripped industrial

capacity by a large margin and at least five types could be found in service at the same time. The problems for the supply and repair organisations cannot have been eased by this variety but in one respect at least they must have been thankful, which was that all used the same ammunition. In almost every other aspect they were different, but matters were again helped by the fact that the German army tended to issue one type to one particular type of formation. For instance the Waffen SS equipped itself almost entirely with the Bergmann design. This was referred to as the Bergmann MP 35. All German sub-machine guns were classified by the letters 'MP' which stood for *Machinen Pistole*, and two figures representing the year of the model. So the Bergmann was the machine pistol model 1935. It had been used in the Spanish Civil War in quite large numbers, and some are reported to have been bought by Ethiopia. It looked very like the Beretta in that the stock was

44

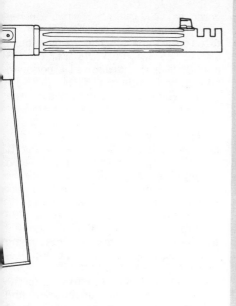

wood, in one piece extending half way along the barrel and the barrel was also quite long and covered by a perforated steel jacket. The magazine was a departure from the accepted norm as it projected from the right hand side although it was in every other way similar to usual practice. Quite why the Bergmann designer chose to put the magazine in this awkward place is no longer clear, and it has never been copied. A probable explanation is that he intended the firer to use the right hand only for both operations of loading and cocking, leaving the left hand to hold the weapon steady. However, the SS appeared to have no trouble with it, and about 40,000 were made for them and used until the end of the war.

The Erma was another design which appeared on the inventory in 1939. It was the 1936 model, and the last of

mm Bergman MP 34 (also known as he MP 35) was used extensively by nany arms of the Axis powers

continuous development which went back to 1920. It was in no way extraordinary for its time and followed the usual pattern of a wooden stock, longish barrel, side loading box magazine, weight of about 10 lbs., and fairly refined machining operations in the manufacture. It was distinguished from its fellows by having a wooden pistol grip in front of the trigger for the left hand to hold. The factory ceased production of this model in 1938 and turned over to the MP 38, but plenty of Ermas had been made by that time and they remained in service until about 1943.

The German army, despite the lessons of the Spanish Civil War, did not adopt an approved design of submachine gun until 1938. The Versailles Treaty had led to a section of the General Staff looking upon submachine guns as essentially police weapons and of limited use in a European war such as they were then planning. The slowly growing industry of the Reich was stretched to the limit in producing other weapons and ammunition, and no effort could be spared for these new guns. It was not until one year before the start of the long planned Second World War that it was finally agreed to order a fixed design. By then it was almost too late, and the penalty was paid in the number of other designs which had to be bought to equip all who needed them. The Erma factory was selected to design the required gun, and within a few months produced the familiar compact, snub-nosed purposeful weapon known the world over as the Schmeisser. In fact the gun owes virtually nothing to Hugo Schmeisser at all, and is the result of work on several prototypes by the Erma factory during the early years of the 1930s. The construction was based on the Vollmer, another early German sub-machine gun, and all the patents were held by Erma. Later on a factory, of which Hugo Schmeisser was the general manager, did make the MP 38 and this is how his name may have

come to be associated with the design. German weapons seem to be fated to be known by the wrong names, and in the Second World War the US and British forces showed a perverse brilliance in selecting titles for German armaments which leave the originators puzzled and wondering. The Wehrmacht knew the MP 38 and 40 by those very letters and numbers, but the Allies insisted on calling it the Schmeisser, and so it has remained in popular imagination. As may be realised, this does not please the Erma factory, which still exists.

The MP 38 was the second sub-machine gun to be officially adopted by the German army, the first being the MP 18, adopted in 1918. The requirement for the MP 38 called for a compact, reliable weapon suitable to the needs of infantry, armoured and airborne forces. It was one of the most popular sub-machine guns produced in the war, and was undoubtedly a first class design. It incorporated several features which have appeared in all subsequent guns all over the world, and it was the first to have a successful folding stock. It was also the first to have no wood in its construction. It was expensive to manufacture because of the number of machining operations that were needed, and within two years it was replaced by the MP 40 which was designed for easy and simple factory processes. MP 40 used sheet steel stampings which were brazed or spot-welded together, and plastic for the pistol grip. Very little high grade alloy steel appears in the specification, and the general design allows for sub-assemblies which can be made up by sub-contractors in different factories. This system was revolutionary in small arms manufacture at that time, and it has been copied by almost every other design since that date. Throughout its life the MP 40 underwent several variations but these do not affect the basic design in any way. As first produced in 1940, it contained a few minor improvements on the MP 38, notably in the safety

Above: Armed with a 9mm MP 38/40, a German paratrooper
at Monte Cassino *Below:* NCOs of the Wehrmacht using MP 38/40s
outside Stalingrad

lock for the bolt. In the Polish campaign of 1939 the German army suffered some accidents due to the bolt jumping out of its safety slot at the rear of the receiver, and slamming forward to fire a shot. This was corrected in the MP 40, and some small differences were introduced in the main spring and firing pin. But the only significant exterior change occurred in 1943 when the Erma factory, together with the Steyr factory in Austria, produced a dual magazine. This rather clumsy idea must almost certainly have been produced in response to a demand for greater magazine capacity to compete with the Russian PPSh-41 then being encountered in large numbers on the Eastern Front. As in any war, the grass on the other side of the fence is always greener, and troops will often exchange weapons with their allies because of some imagined or actual advantage therein, and will also go to great lengths to get hold of those enemy weapons which they believe to be better than their own. It is interesting to find that the Germans were bitten by the same bug, and used the PPSh themselves when they could get it. However, the attempt to double the magazine capacity of MP 40 was not a success and it was introduced only in small numbers. It involved a complicated double housing with separate catches and slides and the loaded gun weighed over 12lbs. It really defeated the whole concept of the sub-machine gun.

Over 1,000,000 MP 40s were made during the war years, out of a total of around 2,000,000 sub-machine guns of all types produced by the German and Austrian arms industries. Manufacture was sub-contracted down to the smallest engineering shops in the country, and the variety of markings and numberings is legion. Many thousands have survived, and are found all over the world to the present day.

British sub-machine policy before the Second World War can be described as being one of disinterest, if not downright apathy; and when in 1938 the Birmingham Small Arms (BSA) Company pressed for a decision on whether the British army required sub-machine guns, it was told in a letter from Whitehall that 'the British army saw no need to equip itself with gangster weapons.' It is tempting to hope that the same officer who dictated that remarkable reply was still at his desk two years later when the desperate state of the country led not only to near panic production of the Sten sub-machine gun, but also of any other 'gangster' weapon that could be had. But by then there were no drawings or tools in existence. In 1938 the BSA company had been holding an option on building the Thompson sub-machine gun under licence for seven years, and time was running out. None had been made, and the company was naturally unwilling to spend more money on renewing the licence unless they could be assured of orders. So the drawings and patterns returned to the USA. And so it was that the British government, totally ignoring the lessons of the Spanish Civil War, and the well-advertised infantry armament of the Axis powers, committed its army to war without any sub-machine gun.

The lack was not immediately apparent during the first six months, and it was not until the *blitzkrieg* that the truth dawned. Scrambling back from Dunkirk to face an imminent German invasion, the British desperately needed thousands of sub-machine guns. They got a few hundred from the USA in the shape of Thompsons, but production of these was not by any means enough, the factory was only geared to peace-time needs, and anyway the gun fired a type of ammunition which was foreign to the British, and so that had to be bought also. Matters were not helped by the fact that the French had got in first in 1939 with an order for over 3,000 guns and 3,000,000 rounds of ammunition Thompsons remained in service until late on in the war, often in the small units of the Commando or similar special forces, but in general service they were quickly replaced by the only native British sub-machine gun design. This was the Sten.

The Sten was a weapon conceived in a climate of extreme emergency. The German *blitzkrieg* had only just failed to destroy the entire British army, and now for the first time in a thousand years an invasion was not only likely, but imminent. It was a frightening situation, and the national bogeyman was the German parachutist wearing a swastika-marked helmet, a loose jumping overall, and carrying a folded MP 38. The apparent ubiquity of the parachute forces and the enormous fire-power of their automatic weapons converted the British almost overnight into sub-machine gun enthusiasts. The only effective counter, so it seemed, were similar weapons. The Sten was designed and developed at the Royal Small Arms Factory at Enfield in early 1941 by two men, R V Shepperd and H J Turpin, and the initial letters of their surnames were coupled with the first two letters of the factory to give the name of the gun. A captured MP 40 was examined, and from it was taken the idea of stamping out as many parts as possible, and also of designing components that could be sub-contracted for manufacture. The over-riding features had to be ease of manufacture, simplicity of operation, and the use of easily available materials. The resulting gun must have appalled the traditional gun makers. It was crude in the extreme, and the early models were noted for stoppages and malfunctions. It was variously dubbed 'The Woolworth gun', 'The plumber's delight', 'The stench gun', and some other less polite and repeatable names.

The great weakness of the Sten was its feed, and this weakness was never eliminated throughout its life. It was

Though unusually kitted-out, Sergeant C Bennet of the 1st Airlanding Brigade still holds his Sten gun

*Above:* Various models of the Sten sub-machine gun, a weapon which because of its manufacture was subject to many permutations *Below:* stripped Mark V

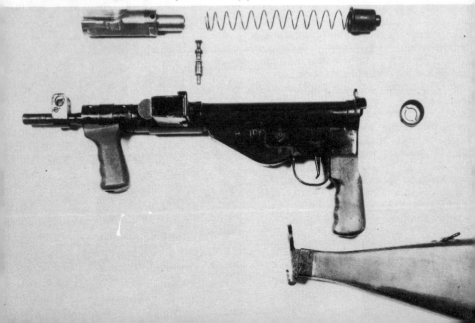

alleged by one disgruntled user to jam every time he tried to fire it, and another said that there had never been anything like it since the Gatling gun. By and large the troops who used it never had complete confidence in it, and those formations who could evade the army equipment system, such as Commandos and special raiding forces, preferred to keep the Thompson. It might be heavier but it was immensely reliable and robust. The Sten's trouble lay in its magazine. This was a staggered row of rounds in a box, feeding to narrow lips which forced each round to move into exactly the same position in order that the bolt could strip it out. Few weapons retain this system now, as it is far better to allow the rounds to come up to the top of the magazine more or less in the same staggered rows as they lie, and the bolt is designed so that it can pick up a round from one side or the other. This is difficult to explain without seeing the two types of magazine, but an analogy can be made with road traffic. Imagine two columns of traffic approaching side by side to an obstruction in the road, and only one vehicle at a time can pass the obstruction; with the Sten feed system both rows of vehicles will have to merge into one just before the obstruction, with all the juggling, hooting, swearing, and delay that such a manoeuvre involves. The dual feed system allows each row to come right up to the obstruction and allows one car from each, in turn, to pass. Obviously the latter is a much easier way of doing it, and gives less trouble.

The single feed magazine requires more push from the bolt to feed a round, and the most common cause of stoppage in the Sten was failure to get a round to the breech. The next most common was to find two rounds stuck in the feedway, and this was caused by a damaged magazine allowing two rounds to feed together. Another drawback to this single feed magazine is that it is virtually impossible to load it without some form of tool to press down the rounds while the top one is fed in. The first two or three are easy, but after that a lever has to lock on to the box and be rocked over to force the others down to give space for the remainder to be slid in one by one. Both the MP 38 and the MP 40 had this type of magazine, and both had the same troubles, though to a lesser degree, as more care was taken in the making of their magazines. All told, there were five Marks of Sten, produced during the war, all differing from each other in minor respects, but all retaining the essential features of the first one. The final one, the Mark 5, fitted a wooden stock and fore pistol grip in an effort to improve the 'Woolworth's' image, and a rifle foresight and bayonet lug were hung on the muzzle. $1\frac{1}{2}$lbs. of extra weight was added by these 'improvements', and handiness was not enhanced.

The 9mm calibre is said to have been arrived at more by good fortune than conscious effort. The campaign in Eritrea had yielded large quantites of captured Italian 9mm ammunition. Ammunition was desperately short, yet nothing in British service used 9mm. It was suggested, incredibly in Whitehall, that the new Sten might be designed to take it, and so it came about. The first gun was made in June of 1941, and in July BSA was asked to quote for its manufacture. Drawings were delivered in a few days and the first gun was required within five weeks! BSA managed to make twenty-five within a month, and from then on was the principle manufacturer together with Enfield. The Sten is made up from sheet metal tubing and simple stampings held together by welding, riveting or pins. All items can be made on simple machinery, and BSA sub-contracted to firms which in peace-time had made lawn mowers, jewellery, ironmongery and children's toys to name but a few items. Finally, both BSA and Enfield built special plant for Sten manu-

*Above:* A 9mm Mark II Sten gun
in the hands of the Free French.
*Right:* A Maquisard in action
with a Mark II Sten with
frame-type buttstock

facture and assembly. Exactly how
many were made is not now easy to
say, but the total wartime production
of sub-machine guns in Britain topped 4,000,000, and it is safe to guess
that over 3,000,000 of these would be
Stens. It is known that more than
2,000,000 of the Mark 2 version alone
were made, and BSA produced 400,000
of the Mark 1 and Mark 2.

The Mark 2 Sten was the workhorse
of the type, and it not only equipped
the British forces, but it was also
parachuted into the occupied countries of Europe in enormous quantities.
Resistance groups in France, the Low
Countries, Scandanavia and Poland
all relied on the Sten for their firepower, and some were supplied as far
afield as Indo-China and Malaya.
Simplicity and robustness made it
ideal for the job, and it was so cheap
that it could be given away to allies in
large numbers. A Mark 2 made in

Britain cost fractionally less than US
$11 altogether, which was roughly
£2·75 at the prevailing rate of exchange. No other weapon in the
Second Word War came down to such a
price, and many came nowhere near it
by a huge margin. The barrel of the
Mark 2 unscrewed, either for cleaning
or storage, and the magazine housing
rotated to form a dustcover over the
ejection opening. The single tube
shoulder stock was removed by press-
ing a catch on the rear of the body, and
the sights were set for 100 yards.
There was no adjustment either for
range or for line. It was meant for
close range fighting, and that was

precisely how it was used. An all-up weight of 8lbs with a full magazine meant that it could easily be carried, and the fact that it disassembled so quickly enabled it to be transported in every sort of bag, case, and pocket on a thousand clandestine operations in Europe. Ammunition could be found anywhere where there were Axis troops, and the Sten, for all its drawbacks, must be considered to be one of the leading war-winning weapons along with the Jeep, Dakota, and the four-engined bomber.

The Lanchester was a sub-machine gun produced exclusively for the Royal Navy. It was never issued to land forces, and never used in action in large numbers. It seems that all navies tend to be independent in their armament procurement, and the case of the Lanchester bears this out admirably. It was designed by George Lanchester in early 1941 and manufactured at the Sterling Engineering Works, who made all that were produced in the country. Lanchester's design was a complete copy of the German MP 28, differing from it only in such minor matters as the attachment of the bayonet, the position of the selector lever, and the sights. The MP 28 was a development of the original MP 18 of the First World War, and in outward appearances there is little to choose between the 1918 design and Lanchester's 1941 model so that the latter was really a remarkable throwback into history. The loaded Lanchester weighed just 12lbs, and was fairly expensive to make, for the usual reasons which apply to all the early sub-machine gun designs. The one piece stock was made of walnut, shaped to resemble the Lee Enfield Number 1 rifle, and fitted with a brass butt plate. The whole effect is one of antiquity for the period in which it was produced, and this is further encouraged by the fact that the magazine housing is solid brass! Nevertheless, the Lanchester served its purpose well and remained in use in naval ships until quite recent times. The box magazine held fifty rounds which is unusual, but was specified for

the MP 28. For the few occasions when sailors needed to use small arms the Lanchester was adequate. By being a design separate from the army's it was not subjected to their over-riding demands, and by being manufactured almost privately the supply could be assured. Had the gun ever been used in quantity in land actions it would not have lasted for long in its original form, indeed it might never have been accepted at all.

Although the United States was the third country in the world to develop a sub-machine gun it was not adopted by the US armed forces until 1928, when a few were used by the Marines in Nicaragua. At about this time also the Coast Guards used some in their efforts to stop bootleggers running illegal cargoes of drink into the country. The weapon they used was the 1928 version of the original 1919 Thompson gun, which already had a world wide reputation from the battles of the American gangsters and the police. Indeed, by the early 30s the 'Tommy Gun' was widely regarded in the USA and Britain as a police weapon only, and by 1939 it is likely that no more than 20,000 had been made altogether. The patent holders were a firm called The Auto-Ordnance Corp and they had no factory, but leased the manufacturing licences to whoever would build. When the big wartime orders began to come across the Atlantic, Colt and Savage Arms Corp collected most of the sub-contracts, but in 1941 the US Government stepped in with its Lease-Lend contracts and controlled the Thompson production until it ceased in 1943. By that time Savage had made 1,500,000 of them, and the total output of all contracts must have been close to 2,000,000. Not all were shipped to Europe by any means, and many of those which were are still in their crates on the Atlantic sea-bed, for the U-boat campaign reached its peak of sinkings at the time of the maximum shipments of 'Tommy guns' to Britain. The US Army took a good share of the production to equip its own forces, and from their experience two simplified and cheaper versions were designed and made.

The original Thompson of 1919 owed nothing to any other design, and it is quite likely that the designers had no knowledge at all of the Beretta and Schmeisser guns which appeared at the same time on the other side of the Atlantic. Typically, the Thompson uses the pistol cartridge of its country of origin, and this, of course, is the .45 rimless. The system of operation was a form of retarded blowback, known as the Blish principle, and worked by utilising the friction between two inclined planes to delay the opening of the breech. A certain amount of advertising capital was made out of this feature, and service users were taught to clean and maintain the sliding 'H' piece, which was the essential part, with some care. In fact its value was doubtful, some venturesome spirits left it out of their weapons altogether without any ill effects on either the gun or the rate of fire, and the later models took official notice of this fact and discarded it. From the very first prototype the Thompson had the distinctive twin pistol grips with their prominent finger notches and steep backward rake and a finned barrel for better cooling. It also offered a choice between a box magazine and the well known 50-round circular drum. If the contemporary films and newspapers of the 1920s can be regarded as any authority upon the social habits of their environment, it would seem that no self respecting gangster or policeman ever fitted the box magazine, and he generally fired his entire drum load in one burst, from the waist. It is, therefore, hardly surprising in some ways that the 1929 *British Textbook of Small Arms* lists the Thompson as being a weapon 'mainly for Police work'.

Yet the Auto-Ordnance Corp had had

**An early model Thompson sub-machine gun with vertical fore grip and drum magazine in use with the British army**

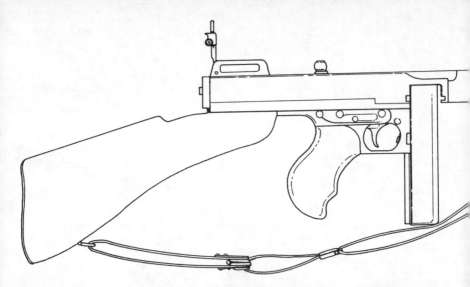

Model 1928 Al Thompson Sub-Machine Gun; *Calibre:* .45; *System of Operation:* Delayed blowback. Selective fire; *Length:* 33.7 inches; *Barrel Length:* 10.5 inches; *Feed Device:* 20 or 30 Round staggered row. Detachable box magazine. 50 Round Drum; *Sights: Front:* Blade; *Rear:* Leaf with aperture notched battle sight; *Weight:* 10.75 lbs; *Muzzle Velocity:* 920 feet per second; *Cyclic Rate:* 600.725 rpm

**Infantrymen armed with Browning automatic rifles and Thompsons in the Far East**

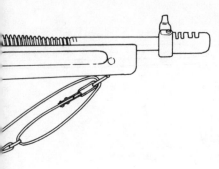

ideas for military use, and in 1923
offered a neat army version without
the forward pistol grip, and with a box
magazine of twenty rounds, a bayonet,
sling, and reputedly a bandolier. It
didn't sell, and they returned to their
standard model. The model 1928, which
was issued in 1940, weighed 12lbs with a
loaded 50-round drum and could hardly
be described as a handy sized weapon.
The wooden shoulder stock could be
removed to reduce the length, but to
fire it without this piece of furniture
produced some pretty erratic shooting.
The Thompson shot a heavy bullet,
and this gave it a strong tendency to
throw its burst of fire high and to the
right. The gun was not easy to hold
onto a small target when firing automatic, and the designers had tried to

*Top:* Tank crew member armed with a
Thompson. *Bottom:* A British soldier
uses his Thompson at Monte Cassino

overcome this with a compensator on the muzzle. This device was a tube with slots cut into the upper half so that some propellant gas was directed upwards as it left the barrel. The idea is called a Cutts compensator, and it gives a downward push to the muzzle with each shot. Unfortunately, this push is not enough to make a great deal of difference, and later models abandoned it. The 50-round drum magazine was awkward to carry and even more awkward to load. The rounds had to be fed in one by one, and when all were in place a clockspring was wound up with a special key. The drum was susceptible to mud and dirt, and more easily damaged than a simple 20-round box. Finally, not every firer needed fifty rounds in the magazine.

In 1941 the US Government simplified the Thompson design, dropping the Blish retarding mechanism, the compensator, the barrel cooling fins and the 50-round drum. The revised model was known as the M 1 and is easily distinguished from the original by another innovation – the forward pistol grip was replaced by a straight horizontal piece of wood. But even a simplified Thompson was too expensive and time consuming to make in wartime, and from the moment that it took over the Lease-Lend contracts the US Government was looking for another design. Throughout 1941 the Aberdeen Proving Grounds examined one idea after another, all good enough in their way, but none of any outstanding merit, and the one which was chosen was the result of a combination of effort in a design team largely sponsored from Aberdeen. This was the M 3, a stubby, ugly, very simple little gun accepted in December 1942. It had a folding wire stock, a tubular receiver, a short barrel, box magazine, and no wood anywhere. The forward handgrip was the magazine housing, the safety catch was the ejection opening cover, and there was no selection lever as the gun only fired automatic. The rate of fire was un-

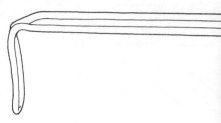

**M3 Sub-Machine Gun**; *Calibre:* .45; *System of Operation:* Blowback, Automatic; *Length:* Stock Extended: 2? inches; Stock Retracted: 22.8 inches; *Barrel Length:* 8 inches; *Feed Device:* Round, In-line detachable box magazin *Sights: Front:* Blade. *Rear:* Fixed aperture; *Weight:* 7.15 lbs; *Muzzle Velocity:* 920 feet per second

usually slow, at about 350-400 round per minute, but this made it muc easier to hold than the Thompson, an so produced more accurate shootin; Everything was meant for mass pr duction, and the Sten was used as basis for much of the design in th direction. A novel feature was the fac that by replacing the barrel, bolt, an magazine and housing, the gun wou. fire 9mm Parabellum ammunitio and the whole conversion took only very few minutes without speci tools. Conventional thinking w; finally outraged beyond redemptio by the M 3A1 model of 1944 in which t; cocking handle was replaced by t; firer's finger! To cock the weapon t; ejection port was opened, a fing stuck into a hole made for the purpo in the bolt, and the bolt hauled to t; rear. The idea is simplicity itse. foolproof and safe. It is strange th no other gun has copied it.

The 'grease gun', as the M 3A1 w; usually called, had several other no elties besides the cocking slot; vario

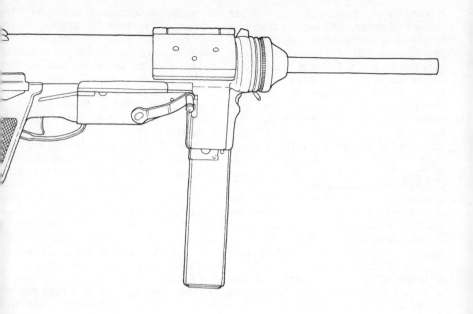

A US marksman tests the M3 sub-machine gun, commonly known as the 'Grease Gun'

removable parts could be used as tools to take off other bits, and a bracket on the back of the receiver could be used as a magazine filler. This last was very necessary, for the M 3 and M 3A1 both used a single feed magazine similar to the Sten. For some reason, probably because of a heavier bolt, stoppages were not so frequent. The design was sound enough to warrant a further manufacturing order for the Korean War, a silenced version was made, mainly for the OSS in Europe, and some fitted a flash hider.

The Soviet Union decided on the use of sub-machine guns rather earlier than the rest of Europe, and produced its first military design in 1934. This was the PPD 34, designed by Degtyarov, and owing something to the MP 28 of Hugo Schmeisser in general shape and operation, and a good deal to the Finnish Suomi in the magazine and ammunition feed. Like all its contemporaries, it was a wooden stocked weapon with a fairly long barrel by today's standards and a loaded weight of 12lbs. This weight is, of course, excessive for the task the weapon has to do, but it meant that considerable strength could be built into the design, and as it included the loaded magazine, it also meant that a respectable reserve of ammunition could be carried without having to reload, or change magazines. The round which the PPD 34 fired was the same as used by all subsequent Soviet designs, namely the 7.62 rimless pistol round, or the 7.63mm Mauser, the two being identical. This round was the standard Soviet pistol ammunition at the time of adoption, and is still very common in the Soviet Bloc. The case is nearly as big as the 9mm, but the bullet is smaller. To meet this smaller bullet the case is reduced in diameter just before it reaches it, producing in effect a 'neck' in the cartridge shape. The sides of the case remain parallel before and after the neck, so allowing the usual blowback principle to be followed. The bullet itself is, of course, lighter than the 9mm, but the muzzle velocity is higher because of the amount of power in the propellant. In other words, in the 7.62mm cartridge there is more propellant per ounce of bullet than in the 9mm, and so the bullet travels faster. Unfortunately, it does not do so for as long as one might like; being a lighter bullet it loses its momentum more quickly than the heavier brands, and so has a shorter effective range. How much this is relevant it is difficult to say because the useful range of a sub-machine gun is so short anyway that matters of bullet flight and so on tend to be more academic than practical. PPD 34 was cheerfully sighted up to 500 metres using a tangent backsight, thereby following the fashion of the day, but it probably never used this facility.

PPD 34 lasted until late 1940 when it was replaced by PPD 40, which was no more than a simplification of the design, little different in outline or operating characteristics. Both of these models were expensive to make and used good quality steel in most of the parts. One interesting point is the chroming of the barrel. This started a fashion for Soviet weapons which has continued to the present day, and while it undoubtedly adds to the cost of the barrel it does also help to preserve it and lengthen its life by resisting corrosion and abrasion. PPD 40 lasted only until 1941, and was a stop gap while the Soviet army steadily carried out a prolonged series of tests to find a suitable replacement.

In 1941 the final design was selected a product of another famous Soviet mind, George Shpagin. His was destined to be the weapon which became synonymous with the Russian soldier and with the communist rule in general, the PPSh-41. This is the weapon which was carried by more Russian soldiers than any other in their armoury; it is the one which appears in almost every picture of Soviet mili

**Winter kit, Eastern Front; a Russian officer armed with a PPSh M 1941 sub-machine gun**

tary actions of the war. It probably did as much to bring about the victory on the Eastern Front as any other single weapon or combination of weapons. 5,000,000 were made by 1945, and production continued afterwards, not only in Russia, but all over the Communist Bloc countries. PPSh was always called by its initial letters as 'Pay-Pay-Shah', and was not really a remarkable design in any way. In general outline it is not strikingly dissimilar from its predecessors, featuring the usual wooden stock, long barrel, perforated barrel jacket, and drum magazine. The weight was the same at 12lbs, but the rate of fire was put up to 900 rounds per minute. It was also more accurate and easier to hold on automatic fire than the PPD series, largely because the bolt was more carefully designed and balanced to its spring, and some care was taken to get the buffer right. A form of compensator was built into the muzzle by sloping the end of it to deflect the muzzle blast, but, like all other compensators, this was hardly effective and its most noticeable result was to increase noise. The mechanism was further simplified, and field stripping consisted of little more than opening the receiver and taking out the bolt. Daily maintenance was restricted to cleaning and oiling, and the ruggedness of the parts was such that it could last for long periods without even this simple treatment. Mud, dirt, water, ice and snow appeared to have no ill effects upon its working, and there was a sufficient reserve of strength in the component parts to stand up to almost indefinite brutality by the user.

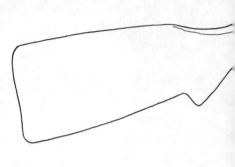

Like all other designs of the war years, the demands of easy manufacture were apparent in the specification, and much of PPSh is crude and rough by comparison with its pre-war forebears. Stampings were much used, and the entire weapon is either seamed, welded or pinned together, but the chromed barrel is retained, and so is the drum magazine. The magazine was, in fact, refined slightly from each successive design of Soviet submachine guns, but the general system remained the same. It carried seventy-one rounds, and was really very old in conception. Loading was a complicated procedure involving removing one of the cover plates, winding the spring, locking up the spring, inserting each round individually, releasing the spring under control, replacing the cover plate, and straightening the first round or two to be pushed out. A tedious performance and not one which a soldier would lightly undertake. There were several hazards in the path of the person loading, not the least being the danger of releasing the spring while putting in the rounds, thereby damaging the magazine and the fingers in different, but serious, proportions. Nevertheless, it served its purpose well, and the alternative 35-round box magazine is rarely seen in pictures or heard of in any accounts.

PPSh dominated the Russian submachine gun scene for the whole war, but it didn't quite have a total mono-

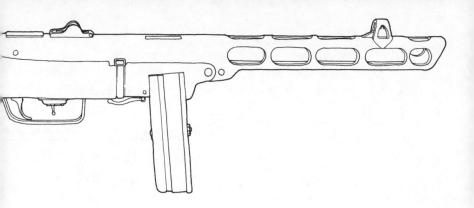

PPS M 1943 Sub-Machine Gun; *Calibre:* 7.62mm; *System of Operation:* Blowback. Automatic only; *Weight with Magazine:* 7.98 lbs; *Length with Stock:* 32.72 inches; *Length with Stock Folded:* 24.25 inches; *Barrel Length:* 9.45 inches; *Feed Device:* 35 Round box magazine; *Sights: Front:* Post with ears; *Rear:* 'L' Type; *Cyclic Rate:* 650 rpm

Russian mounted troops equipped with the inevitable PPSh M 1941

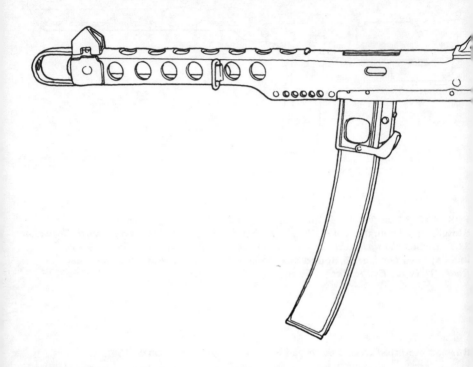

poly. There was another type produced in some quantity, this being the PPS 42. PPS 42 appeared in a slightly unusual way, as it was designed, produced, and used during the seige of Leningrad. There was an acute shortage of sub-machine guns in the city, and when the Germans surrounded it the supply of weapons from Russia was all but cut off. An engineer by the name of Sudarev designed a sub-machine gun and had it made in a Leningrad arms factory. As they were produced so they were issued to the troops, and field testing was done in battle. Despite this atmosphere of drama surrounding the birth of the PPS 42, it was a sound and sensible design which was highly effective in use. It was entirely metal in construction except for the pistol grip, where either wood or plastic was used, and, of course, ease of manufacture was paramount. The gun only fired auto-

matic, and a box magazine holding thirty-five rounds was fitted. Presumably the 71-round drum was beyond the resources of the Leningrad factory, and even when the PPS 42 grew up into the PPS 43 and was issued on quite a large scale after the siege, the box magazine was retained. The latter model was a refinement of the 42, with modifications incorporated from battle experience, but it was very little different. Both models had a folding metal stock, a sheet metal muzzle brake, and weighed only 8½lbs. One can only presume that they failed to oust the PPSh for reasons of standardisation, for by 1943 the numbers of PPSh in use was already several millions, and it was obviously unwise to try and replace them with another type. Even so, quite large numbers of PPS 42 and 43 were made, probably in excess of a million.

Although the Soviets contributed

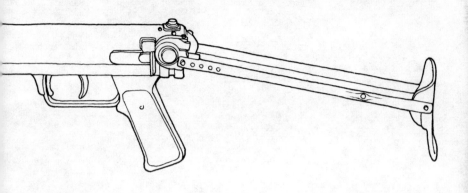

PS M 1943 Sub-Machine Gun; *Calibre:* 7.62mm; *System of Operation:* ...owback. Automatic only; *Weight with Magazine:* 8.5 lbs; *Length with Stock:* ...2.72 inches; *Length with Stock Folded:* 24.25 inches; *Barrel Length:* 9.45 ...ches; *Feed Device:* 35 Round box magazine; *Sights: Front:* Post with ears; ...ear: 'L' Type; *Cyclic Rate:* 650 rpm

...ery little in the direction of design to ...e fund of international knowledge, ...one respect at least they led the world ...om 1942 onwards. This was in the ...mployment and tactical use of the ...ub-machine gun. No one else display-...l such incredible drive, energy and ...ass force with their weapons, and ...is was nowhere better shown than in ...e tank rider battalions. A battalion ...these men was about 500 strong, and ...ery man with the same weapon, ...mely the PPSh-41: in the war-time ...ndbooks of uniforms they are shown ...wearing a cossack type astrakhan ...t, a blue belted smock, grey riding ...eeches and soft black leather boots. ...fact they probably wore something ...r more workmanlike, and in action ...ey obviously all had steel helmets ...their heads. But all had a PPSh in ...eir hands, and several drum maga-...nes in pouches around their waists. ...ney provided the immediate infantry

support for an armoured division, and each squad rode on its own individual tank. When that tank was knocked out the survivors climbed onto an-other, and when that was knocked out – and many were – onto a third or a fourth. They must have suffered unbe-lievable losses in every assault, al-though just how many will never be known as the Soviets are not eager to publish details of their war-time unit casualties, even if they know them, and that seems unlikely in view of their record system which was, to say the least, elementary. Just to travel on the outside of a tank in peacetime on straight and level ground is frighten-ing enough, to do it in an assault, in the face of enemy fire, on unknown ground, at high speed, with the tank gun firing and the turret traversing seems little short of suicidal – and it quite likely was. The life expectancy of a tank rider cannot have been any

*Above:* Soviet infantry in winter camouflage ride their tanks to battle
*Below:* Russian tank-riders prepare to engage the Germany army

better than the two or three weeks quoted for the First World War subaltern, and the quality of the men and their attitude to life reflected this hazardous job. One British officer who met a battalion of them in 1945 described them as being very little better than animals with an almost total disregard for human life or suffering, and a simple and brutal disciplinary system. Their supply arrangements, to quote this one source, appeared to be based on looting and capture, though common sense demands that ammunition must have been provided, and therefore some sort of administrative arrangements were in being. Desperate times breed desperate measures, and the tank riders did not last long after the war ended.

The tactics of the tank riders were simple in the extreme, and their training was equally simple. The only manoeuvre of war which they practised was the attack. Their only reaction on encountering any opposition, no matter how large or daunting, was to charge into it, either on foot, or on their tanks. Weather made no difference nor did casualties, and there are some propaganda photos and film of tank riders assaulting through deep snow and intense cold, hanging on to the handles on the outside of their tanks, wearing white oversuits and hoods. Equally, they hung on through the dust and grime of the long summer attacks through the Ukraine and the Don Basin, and over the Polish plains, their PPShs slung over their shoulders by a webbing strap, and a small haversack at the waist.

Of course, there were other, less glamorous infantry units also armed with PPSh, following the usual Soviet war-time practice of training a man in one weapon only to save time. Thus, there were whole infantry companies with sub-machine guns, and paratroops in particular carried a very high proportion of PPSh. In fact, an unusually high proportion of the Soviet army was armed with sub-machine guns, far more than in any of the Axis or other Allied armies, and they all used it vigorously. One cannot use a sub-machine gun like a rifle; it is no good lurking behind a hedge and hoping to snipe at troops crossing the field in front, nor is it any good to take pot shots at some fleeting figure on a distant skyline, one has to get up, get in, and get at it. It is the weapon of a determined and energetic man, almost like a long range bayonet, and it carries much of the same shock effect.

The final part of the sub-machine gun story covers the smaller contributions, notably those of the Finns and the Japanese, though the Japanese can hardly be said to have contributed much. The Finnish army had had a sub-machine gun in service for some years before the war, and used it in the proper tactical way. A noted arms designer named Lahti made his first sub-machine gun in the early 1920s, and successively developed it until 1931 when the 9mm model appeared. This was a practical and effective weapon which was produced under licence in Sweden, Denmark, and Switzerland. Their output was sold all over the world and used in the Gran Chaco War of 1932, and the Spanish Civil War. The model of 1931 was the usual sort of sub-machine gun for the period, being carefully and expensively made, fitted with a long wooden stock, and a somewhat long barrel covered by a perforated jacket. It was unusual in two respects. The first was its weight which was 12lbs, and by most standards of its day, excessive. However, this weight contributed greatly to a steadiness when firing automatic and led to accurate shooting in which the present day models still excel.

The second feature was the magazine. This was the now familiar 71-round drum. How much this drum owed to the Thompson is not easy to say, but it seems obvious that the idea must at least have derived from the US design. It would probably not have survived beyond the start of the war had not the Soviets adopted it so

**The Suomi contributed to the defeats of the Soviets in the early stages of the Russo-Finnish campaign of 1940**

whole-heartedly for their PPD and PPSh series. The Finns knew how to use their Suomi sub-machine guns, and in the Winter War of 1939/40 they held and defeated a far larger Soviet army by sheer skill and determination, in which was included a sensible and aggesive employment of the sub-machine gun. They were carried by ski patrols and infiltrating parties who swooped out of the forests onto the unprepared Russian rear areas, mowed down a score or two of men, set fire to trucks, tents and stores, and disappeared back into the trees. They were also used in quick, murderous little hand-to-hand actions in the darkness and undergrowth between advance parties of both sides, in ambushes, in withdrawals, and in the few actual all-out battles in which the numerically inferior Finnish army stood up to and faced the fumbling, inefficient Russian steamroller. The Soviet losses were enormous in that short war, and not least was the loss to their prestige and self respect. The Soviet army had been shown to the world to be bad, if not almost totally incompetent. But they learned quickly, and one of the lessons was the proper way to use a sub machine gun. The Winter War contri buted in no small way to the intense testing programme that was conduc ted throughout 1940, and culminated in the PPSh of 1941, so it can be said that in a very unwitting and indirect way the Finns made a significant and dramatic contribution to the Allied victory of 1945.

While design was novel and practical in the frozen north of the world, it was practically stagnant in the Far East. The Japanese army did not even look at a sub-machine gun until 1936, although marines of the Imperial Japanese Navy had a had few Swiss built Bergmanns in the early 30s. The army left these alone, and tested its own design, the Model 1, which used the weak 8mm Japanese pistol round.

Model 1 was not a success, nor was Model 2 which followed in 1937 firing a .5mm special round. By 1940 an improved Model 3, known as the Type 100, was accepted. It was still not entirely satisfactory, and throughout the war research continued into improvements to it which resulted in the final Type 00, referred to as the Type 100 (1944). The Type 100 reverted to the unsatisfactory 8mm round, and this was doubtless the main cause of all its troubles. The weapon was nearly three feet long, shaped much like a rifle, and made by the usual machining operations which were popular at the time. Much attention was paid to fixing a bayonet below the muzzle, for which a special lug and strengthening piece was provided. It only fired automatic, and that at the unusually slow rate of 50 shots per minute. The box magazine fed thirty rounds from the left side, and the sights could be set for the unbelievable maximum range of 1,500 metres. Overall weight was low at just over 8½lbs, and this is about the one good feature of what can only be described as a poor and unadventurous design. How many were made is not known, but it does not appear to have been issued in any significant numbers. This, again, is surprising, as the sub-machine gun is the jungle weapon *par excellence*, and one which one would have expected the Japanese High Command to have demanded in large quantities for their long planned Pacific War. Japanese paratroops were one of the few categories of soldier who carried the Type 100, and a special folding stock version was made for them. In this the stock was cut

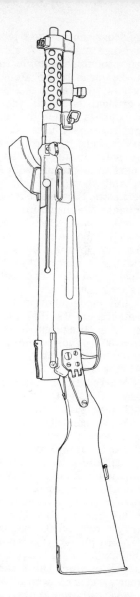

**Type 100 Sub-Machine Gun (with folding stock);** *Calibre:* **8mm;** *System of Operation:* **Blowback. Automatic only;** *Length:* **34 inches;** *Length with Stock Folded:* **22.2 inches;** *Barrel Length:* **9 inches;** *Feed Device:* **30 Round staggered row. Detachable box magazine;** *Sights: Front:* **Barleycorn with ears;** *Rear:* **Tangent with notch;** *Weight:* **7.3 lbs;** *Muzzle Velocity:* **Approx 1,100 feet per second;** *Cyclic Rate:* **450 rpm**

through just behind the trigger guard and a hinge inserted. A simple lock held the stock in a straight line and it folded forwards to lie alongside the receiver and barrel. It is always easy to be critical, but of all the methods one can choose for a folding stock this is about the most clumsy, and the one which weakens the gun most. The danger point in any wooden stock is that part immediately behind the receiver and above the trigger guard, where the wood has been cut away to accommodate the mechanism, yet must remain thin enough for the firer's hand to grasp it in comfort. To cut through at this spot means that a very substantial hinge must be fitted to replace the lost strength, and substantial hinges are heavy.

The 1944 model showed definite improvements on its 1940 parent, and among other things the rate of fire was put up to 800 rounds per minute, which was probably a bit high, but undoubtedly better than 450. Much simplification occurred in the manufacturing processes, the sights were fixed at the realistic range of 100 metres, and apart from the wooden stock and bayonet fixing, it was a workmanlike design. But it was too late. Production did not start until mid-1944, and only 8,000 had been made by the time the war ended.

All in all, the story of Japanese submachine guns is a sad and sorry tale of inept design, poor direction from the military, and lost opportunities. There were plenty of weapons in the late 1930s which could have been copied in the way in which the Japanese were so expert, and these would have vastly increased the power and tactical capability of their divisions who fought in the Pacific Islands and the Burmese jungle. For some reason they failed to grasp this basic fact, and the only recorded occasion when sub-machine guns were used in battle in significant numbers was in the airborne assault upon the Dutch oilfields in Sumatra. For this action the Japanese paratroops carried the Type 100 (1940), and it was plainly successful.

However, there was not actually total gloom in the Pacific. There was a lightening in the sky over Australia where a vigorous effort was made in 1940 and '41 to produce a sub-machine gun for the Australian army. No help was forthcoming from either the USA or Britain and it was a case of home production or nothing. As it turned out, the home production was not too bad, and later it became even better. In mid-1941 the Austen appeared, which was, as its name implies, an Australian Sten. Not having seen it, it is difficult to be objective about it, but it looks and sounds to have been a better bet than its parent. It used pure Sten parts except for the folding metal stock, the bolt and the telescoping main spring which were all copied direct from the German MP 40. The only original Australian designing in the gun was the two pistol grips and a better lock for the stock. It worked well and it is now difficult to see why it never caught on, but the fact remains that it did not and only something like 20,000 were made, before it was superseded by the the Owen.

Lieutenant Evelyn Owen designed his gun in late 1940, and it was adopted on 20th November, 1941. By 1944 over 45,000 had been made in three variations of the original Mark 1, and there has never been a Mark 2 in service. Quite large numbers of Owens are still in stock in Australia, and they are carried by the Citizen Army, the Australian reserve force. It is a popular gun, and it is difficult to find any one who has used it who has a word to say against it. It is admittedly large and heavy for a sub-machine gun, though not as heavy as some, and it looks clumsy; nevertheless, it works with incredible reliability, and survives indefinite rough treatment. In the early 1950s it was used by the Australian army in the Malayan anti-terrorist campaign, and was preferred in the jungle by all other troops to the Sten, the Sterling, or the Thompson which latter still existed at that time. In fact, the Australians were contin-

*Top:* Patchett machine carbine 1941 9mm. *Centre:* Owen machine carbine (Australian) 9mm. *Bottom:* Austin machine carbine also of Australian origin and 9mm calibre

y being importuned to 'lose' a gun exchange for almost anything they ed to name!

The Owen owes little to any other n current in 1940, although much of weight comes from the fact that it made by the older processes involv- machining. Inside it is fairly ple, though it incorporates one velty. This is a fixed disc around the in spring guide. The bolt handle is ached to this guide, and is well ind the bolt, which arrangement ts the disc in front of the bolt slot, l so prevents dirt that enters ough that slot from getting to the t slideways. Of course, the ejection t is still open and dirt can get in re, but the feature may have helped earn the Owen its reputation for reme reliability. The other feature ich makes the gun so distinctive is unique top mounted magazine. No er gun tried this idea, but it works l whatever the theoretical objec- ns to it may be, and surprisingly it

does not hamper the firer any more than the usual one does. Perhaps Lieutenant Owen put it on top to help the magazine spring, certainly he did not do so, as has been suggested, because they all walk upside down in Australia; but whatever his reason he knew well what he was doing, despite its strange appearance. The only other features of the Owen were the barrel which was held in place by a quick release plunger, a doubtful advantage since sub-machine guns do not need to change barrels like light machine guns; and a muzzle compensator. It speaks volumes for the design that it went through its life with virtually no changes in the original conception, and earned the respect and praise of all who used it.

# Rifles

The rifle is always supposed to be introduced to the new recruit as his best friend, though until he actually goes into combat it is probably no more popular than the bugler at reveille. It is awkward and heavy to carry, demands continual attention, and is a source of constant trouble from drill sergeants who speculate on the nesting habits of birds and spiders in the barrel. But it is the rifle and its bayonet which, in the hands of its owner, stays on the final piece of real estate while the politicians argue over who shall have it. The whole process was neatly summed up by an American officer who said, 'You can keep your atom bombs, your tanks, and your airplanes; you'll still have to have some little guy with a rifle and bayonet who winkles the other bastard out of his foxhole and gets him to sign the Peace Treaty.' And for this very good reason we have devoted a chapter to the rifle.

In 1939 most of the contestants were armed with bolt action rifles which had been designed in the previous century and differed little from their original models. By and large there was nothing much wrong with this, from the view point of pure performance. All the rifles were roughly similar in their capabilities, though they differed in their construction, and most were well able to fire a bullet with fair accuracy to a distance of half a mile, at which range it still had considerable remaining energy and could do a surprising amount of

**German troops in action armed with the Mauser KAR 98K, the standard carbine of the German army**

damage. All weighed in the region of 9 or 10lbs., had wooden stocks extending all the way up the barrel, and accepted bayonets on to some sort of fastening at the muzzle. Most had a magazine which held five rounds, and all were strong, simple, and straightforward in design. For the most part construction involved a good deal of machining and careful setting up and fitting. They were not particularly cheap to make, but all the manufacturers who were in the arms business were equipped to build military rifles, and had plenty of experience behind them.

This sort of rifle lasts a very long time, and eighty-year-old examples are quite common today, still shooting well after years of hard wear. Provided that they are not abused, they will continue for many more years yet, and this was one of the prime reasons for the apparent anachronism in rifles among the European armies at the start of the war. Their armouries were full of weapons in excellent condition, and to scrap them would be extremely expensive. To change to a more modern design would take time, and in the meantime the war would roll on. Ordnance and supply officers hate change and multiplicity of types (though they do not always get their way, as we shall see later), and, finally, rifles are unglamorous things which tend to be bypassed in the race to keep up with the military Joneses. By 1939 there was not a single tank, aeroplane, or truck of 1918 design or manufacture in service in any European army, yet there were thousands of 1918 rifles and machine guns, indeed my own first military issue weapon was made in 1913, and very good it was, but design had advanced in the intervening years, perhaps not quite as dramatically as with aeroplanes, but, nevertheless, significantly enough.

By 1939 the only logical weapon for an infantryman was a self loading or semi-automatic rifle. There was no lack of designs, and many prototypes had been made, but a hard core of conservatism in most countries kept it out, as well as lack of money, and the arguments put forward against such a rifle read in an almost ghostly way like the arguments that had been put forward eighty or so years before against the breech loading arm. 'Waste of ammunition' was the commonest of all, 'impossibility of controlling fire' another, and 'liability of the mechanism to get out of order', 'difficulty of repairs', and 'difficulty of resupplying ammunition' some of the others. They were all wrong, but the mud of the 1918 trenches was still a powerful memory, and only the simplest mechanism could survive it and continue to work. In Britain the opposition was particularly strong, and it managed for one reason or another to ensure that a semi-automatic rifle did not come into the service until 1957, by which time practically every other army in the world had changed. Throughout the war this retention of the bolt action was a serious ball and chain round the leg of the infantry, since it takes longer to train a useful shot with a bolt rifle than it does with an automatic one.

The rifle with which the British army entered the war was the one with which they had ended the last one, namely the ageing SMLE. These four letters stood for Short Magazine Lee Enfield, adopted for service in 1902, as a shorter and lighter version of the original Lee Enfield of 1895. Between 1902 and 1939 not a great deal had changed, although the latest models made were up to Mark III , which, being interpreted, means that at least six modifications had been incorporated to the original service rifle, and its correct title since 1926, when the British changed their nomenclature, had been Rifle No 1, Mark III , SMLE, .303-inch. There was great affection for this rifle throughout the British and Commonwealth armies, and military legend has tended to endow it with properties which it did not really possess. It was a robust weapon, of simple design, and reasonably handy due to its comparatively short overall length. It fired the outdated .303 inch round which had a rimmed case and all the disadvantages that follow from rims. In fairness to the .303 these disadvantages did not show up too greatly in the rifle itself, but one irritating feature was that some care had to be taken in filling the chargers with which the magazine was usually loaded, as jams could easily be induced if the rims were not in the right order. There were times when this could be embarrassing, to say the least.

The bolt used rear locking lugs, which were never popular in other countries because they are inherently inaccurate. The SMLE design overcame this to some extent by using a heavier receiver, but the truth is that the rifle was never a great success for really pin-point target shooting. Luckily few war-time soldiers are called upon to perform to such fine limits, and even today the quickest way to get frog marched out of an old Comrades' gathering is to suggest that the SMLE could not shoot straight. The rear mounted lugs permitted a short bolt travel to chamber the next round, and there was enough width on the lugs to allow the corners to be well rounded. Couple this with a bit of wear on the rubbing surface and you have the one great feature of the Enfield bolt action – speed. The bolt was remarkably easy to 'manipulate' as the instructors called it, and with a bit of skill and a drop of oil it was possible to fire it much faster than any other bolt rifle.

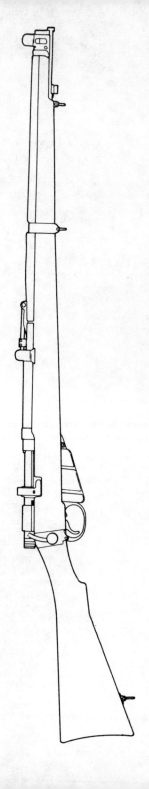

**Rifle No 1 Mark III (Short magazine Lee Enfield);** *Calibre:* .303; *Length* 44.5 inches; *Barrel Length:* 25.19 inches; *Feed Device:* 10 Round detachable box magazine; *Sights: Front:* Blade with protecting ears with notch; *Rear;* Tangent leaf with notch; *Muzzle Velocity:* 2,440 feet per second; *Weight:* 8.62 lbs

*Above:* British troops armed with No 1 Mark IV rifles, fitted with spike bayonets, and Thompsons. *Below:* SMLE and sword-type bayonet

Working the Enfield bolt called for less muscular effort and arm movement than any other rifle, and in its way this led to greater accuracy when firing rapidly because the firer did not get so tired, and the rifle hardly needed to move from the point of aim. Nevertheless, it could never compete with a semi-automatic. The sights were an old pattern of an open 'U' backsight and blade foresight, and recruits took a little time to get used to it. The bayonet was a sword blade type, sixteen inches long and weighing 1½lbs. It differed little from the model of 1888 and affected shooting to a noticeable extent.

The shortcomings of the SMLE had been realised many years before and in 1926 a lighter and simplified version was made. In the First World War too much factory effort had been tied down in making rifles, and in the 1926 variation the needs for re-arming during a period of national emergency were considered and allowed for. Trials continued on the rifle, the final version appearing in 1935, but the pattern was not finally approved until November 1939 when quantity manufacture started. The rifle was then known as the Rifle No 4, Mark 1. Quite naturally, it was not long before Marks 1 and 2 came along, but the variety of marks never climbed beyond 2, and the changes were not significant. The No 4 rifle appeared at a quick glance to be different altogether from the SMLE but in actual fact it was not far away from it in any feature except the bayonet. The barrel was heavier and the bolt lugs were balanced, aperture sights were

Rifle Number 4 Mk I; *Calibre:* .303; *System of Operation:* Manual bolt operated; *Length:* 44.5 inches; *Barrel Length:* 25.2 inches; *Feed Device:* 10 round detachable box; *Front Sights:* Blade with protecting ears; *Rear Sights:* Vertical leaf with aperture battle sight or 'L' type; *Weight:* 8.8 lbs; *Muzzle Velocity:* 2,440 feet per second

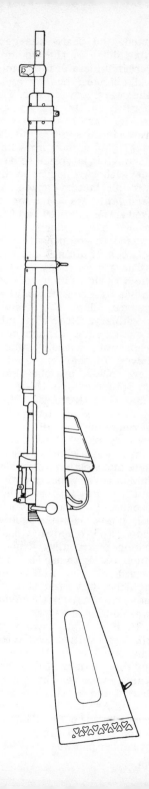

fitted, and there was general slimming down of the woodwork. There were innumerable minor modifications and changes, but by and large the rifles were very similar. The No 4 was more accurate, partly due to the heavier barrel, and partly to an increase in the sight radius. Its aperture backsight found immediate favour, although it later had to be changed to one with two positions due to pressure on factory space. This latter backsight was a horror which gave fixed settings at 300 and 600 yards and needed the bayonet to be fixed or unfixed to compensate for ranges in between. It did not last long.

There were many modifications to the No 4 rifle which were the result of sub-contracting to small firms who had to adapt the design to their machinery. Nearly a million were made at Long Branch near Toronto, who stamped their name on the receiver. In the USA another million were made by the Savage Arms Corporation, and these two million rifles were all Mark 1*, differing from the UK ones by virtue of the method of removing the bolt. Otherwise they were identical. The bayonet for all marks was a short spike eight inches long and weighing only seven ounces. It was never popular with the troops, not from any failings in lethality, but because it was useless for the essentially domestic tasks such as chopping wood and opening tins, for which bayonets are always needed. It was much easier to use than the unwieldy sword of the SMLE for bayonet fighting, but even this virtue could not save it as so little bayonet fighting was done in the war.

In 1944 a cut down version of the No 4 was introduced into service as the No 5 Rifle. It was lighter and smaller than the No 4, the reductions being achieved by shortening the barrel and cutting away some of the stock. About 1½lbs was saved in this way, but the resulting carbine was unpleasant to fire and kicked hard. A rubber pad was fitted to the butt to

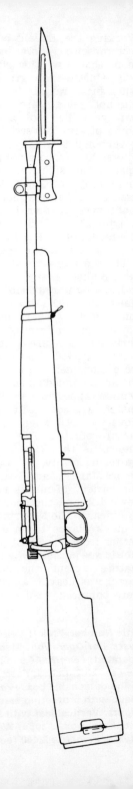

reduce the shock, but another result of weight paring was that accuracy was affected quite markedly, and the sights would not stay zeroed. In the jungle this was of less consequence, but it killed the rifle for post-war service. About 50,000 were made. In its brief life it achieved a notable first by being the first British rifle to be fitted with a flash hider, a fitting called for by the burning gasses ejecting from the shortened barrel. Its light weight and general handiness brought it many exponents, but it was too crude a compromise to last.

Another version of the No 4 was the sniping rifle, the No 4 (T), the (T) standing for telescope. These rifles were selected from the line as being of better accuracy than the standard, and were fitted with a No 32 telescope sight. This telescope had originally been meant for the Bren LMG, but was never used on that gun. The entire production was diverted to sniping. The No 4 made a good sniping rifle, something the SMLE had never done, and it is still in service today, rebarrelled to 7.62mm.

The conservatism in the British army was almost equally matched in Germany, though, as we shall see in the next chapter, as the war progressed, new and revolutionary designs were accepted and produced, but by 1939 there was no real progress from 1918, and the factories were in full blast making bolt action weapons. They never made enough, and the German army equipped itself with a great variety of different rifles as the war went on, picking them up from conquered countries as well as from

allies. However, the accepted or standard rifle was the 7.92mm Kar 98k. It originated in the Model 1898 rifle, which was probably the most successful bolt action rifle ever produced, and which has been used in one form or another in most countries of the world since the turn of the century. The secret of its success lies in its method of locking the bolt, and for this the well known Mauser front locking lugs are used. In this system the lugs are at the extreme front of the bolt head, and turn to lock into an extension of the barrel. There is no firing stress on the bolt, nor on the sides of the receiver, and both can be made lighter than in the Enfield arrangement. The stress path in the breech end is short, and greater accuracy is achieved from this type of barrel. The disadvantage is that the bolt has to be opened and shut along a longer path as it must not only travel the length of the complete round, but the length of the locking extension also. The Mauser bolt is, therefore, not so easy to use for rapid fire. It is also less easy to clean as the locking extensions are difficult to get into, but these are not serious shortcomings.

The Model Kar 98k had been accepted into service in 1935, and in many ways resembled the commercial model Mauser of the time. It was almost exactly the same length and weight as the SMLE, but was generally a little slimmer with less stocking and a protruding muzzle. The backsight was well up the barrel giving a short sight radius. A bayonet bar underneath the muzzle disappeared in the versions made in 1944 and '45, and these models were usually fitted with laminated wooden stocks as the supplies of good wood dried up in Germany. But it is an interesting indication of the demands of modern war that this elderly rifle was still being turned out in the last year of the war, when it had been in production for over nine years, and when one might have expected that enough had been made, and that the

Rifle Number 5 Mk I; *Calibre:* .303; *System of Operation:* Manual bolt operated; *Length:* 39.5 inches; *Barrel Length:* 18.7 inches; *Feed Device:* 10 round detachable box; *Front Sights:* Blade with protecting ears; *Rear Sights:* Vertical leaf with aperture battle sight; *Weight:* 7.15 lbs; *Muzzle Velocity:* 2,400 feet per second

*Above:* The Mauser 98 rifle (probably the most successful bolt action rifle ever produced) and the 98K carbine in action in France, 1940.
*Below:* Motorised infantry with Mauser 98K carbines, one with 'scope

actories might have been making something more modern. In fact, there were never enough rifles to go round, and when the Reich overran Belgium the FN factory in Liège was put to work making the Kar 98k and produced large numbers before it was liberated in 1944. In the same way the Zbrojovka Brno factory in Czechoslovakia made many thousands. These foreign models differed from the original in slight details, but not in the essentials.

The original rifle carried a cleaning rod which was stowed in the fore end underneath the muzzle. One rod was not long enough for one barrel, and three had to be joined together to get the necessary length, an unusual idea, but apparently effective. There were several different models of bayonet, all roughly similar in shape, being a short handy blade which clipped on to the bar under the muzzle. There were several other accessories. One was a winter trigger which the Russian campaign introduced. This was a sheet metal cover which fitted over the trigger guard with an extension which projected behind. By squeezing the extension the trigger was drawn to the rear and fired, and this could easily be done with a hand wearing a large glove. Another standard fitting was a grenade launcher on the muzzle. There were two types, a spigot for firing hollow-based grenades, and a cup. The spigot came into service in 1941 and was used in the North African campaign, but disappeared by early 1942. The grenade it fired was a simple hollow charge anti-armour device and was obviously not successful, since it was so soon replaced. In the following year the cup type appeared, firing a rifled grenade of 3cm calibre. It was called the Schiessbecher, and remained in service until the end of the war. The novelty lay in the idea of firing spin stabilised grenades, in which it is almost unique, since most launchers use fins to keep the projectile steady in flight. The Schiessbecher grenades were inserted with a

twisting motion into the cup, and while perfectly successful within the limited range and accuracy of these missiles, must have been more expensive and troublesome to make than the fin stabilised types. Those who have been on the receiving end of them recall that they gave an eerie whistle while in the air, thereby giving a little warning to those with ears sharp enough to appreciate it. The launcher was accompanied by a sight which is quite sophisticated for these rather crude projectiles, and it was levelled by a small bubble. Nowadays, rifle grenades are going out of favour, but even in their heyday the idea of putting bubble levelled sights was beyond the limits of other designers, and it shows a typical attention to extravagant detail which sometimes appears in German equipment.

The sniping version of the Kar 98k fitted a 4-power telescope which lived up to the high reputation of the German optics industry. It was large and heavy, which is of less importance to a sniper than to other infantrymen, but other models were produced, and different ones at that, so that by 1944 there were so many telescopes in service that output was being affected. A rationalised 'scope was brought out in this year, of 1.5-power, and it was fitted to all rifles which needed it. A variety of brackets allowed it to fit onto both the Kar 98k and the more modern weapons which were by then in service. This 'scope is small and has a long eye relief so that it has to be mounted well forward on the rifle, in the case of the Kar 98k well in front of the breech. Another sniping attachment was a silencer, which was issued on a limited scale in 1944. It was only a partial success, as all silencers are when firing supersonic ammunition, and special low powered ammunition was issued for it. It only appeared on a small scale.

Several millions of these excellent rifles were made and used in the Second World War, but the fact remains that they were out of date before

they ever came into service. The fixed magazine only held five rounds, the bolt action, as has been said, is not best suited to rapid fire, and for specialist troops the size was a distinct disadvantage. An attempt to reduce size and weight in 1940 led to the Gewehr 33/40, specially made for mountain and paratroop divisions. But this was only a stop-gap at best. Recoil increased, just as it did with the Enfield No 5. Muzzle blast was considerable, and the troops disliked it. A version with a folding stock was soon abandoned. While the paratroops took to their troublesome FG 42, the remainder of the army looked to more conventional self loading rifles. Development started early on in the war and by 1941 two different designs were ready for troop trials. These were the Model 41(W) and (M), made by Walther and Mauser respectively. The Mauser contender did not last long, and the Walther rifle went on to be produced in large quantities as the 1943 G 43. The 41(W) was a gas operated weapon in which the bolt was locked by two flaps or lugs being pushed out from the sides of the bolt into recesses in the receiver. A muzzle cone trapped the gas and allowed it to rebound onto a piston which forced a long operating rod to the rear, and this in turn forced the bolt carrier to the rear. The carrier unlocked the lugs, and pulled the bolt back. The whole system is rather heavy and requires fine machining, in which is reflected the design spirit still active at the beginning of the war. Later on rougher methods sufficed. The one piece wooden stock ran right up to the muzzle cap, the magazine held ten rounds, and was fixed to the gun demanding that reloading was by charger through the top of the receiver. The all-up weight was just over 11lbs , which must have been a nasty shock for the men who had to carry it

**Model 43 semi-automatic rifle (G43); though crude in manufacture it was an excellent rifle produced in quantity**

and it was muzzle heavy to shoot.

The G 43 was developed from the 41(W), and was a much better proposition both to the manufacturer and the soldier. It was simply made of stampings, castings and forgings, and only machined in the places where it mattered. The muzzle gas system was dropped, and a similar idea to the Russian Tokarev rifle used in its stead. In this the gas has a shorter path, and weight is saved, but the locking system was retained. The G 43 is a very businesslike rifle, with a one piece three-quarter length wood stock made of laminated beech, a detachable 10-round magazine, and an integral mounting for the ZF 41 telescope. The usual sights were the tangent leaf and barleycorn foresight found on most German rifles, and the telescope was not fitted to all, but to do so required no special modification. It was generally used as a specialist's weapon, as too few were made for general issue, and was often found as a sniper rifle. There was no bayonet, no modifications, and no variations to the original design. Later on in the war the name was changed to Karabiner 43 (K 43), but this indicated no alteration to the pattern beyond a few obvious short cuts such as a plastic hand guard. It seems to have been a fairly reliable weapon, but, although ranking about third in numbers and importance among self loading rifles of the war, it contributed nothing to design and has not been followed up since 1945. The G 43 is the last of the German rifles to be examined, although much effort was expended on other automatic rifles, but these are more properly assault rifles, which demand a study all to themselves. To write a fair epitaph on German rifles of the second World War is difficult, but it might be summed up by saying it was a case of too little at first, and too much later. There was too little research and development during the twenties and early thirties, so that when it became imperative to rearm the only design that could possibly be put into production was the outdated Kar 98k, and too much diversity of effort later, leading to a competition between rival designs for the limited factory space left intact by the bombing. After reading the story of the assault rifles it is easy to see that a firm decision taken in 1940 or '41 could have put the Reich well in the lead in the small arms field for the whole war. But history is full of similar stories and without them authors would be looking for some other way to make a living.

Luckily for the US Army, firmness in decision making had been a virtue long enjoyed in the Department of Defence. For the most part this had been negative decision where small arms was concerned, but there was an encouraging change in 1932 when General Douglas MacArthur endorsed the results of trials at Aberdeen Proving Grounds which showed the self loading rifle designed by John Garand to be superior to any others seen and tried. General MacArthur also stipulated that the .30-06 cartridge was to be retained, and here he was equally sensible, for enormous stocks of this round existed, and to have gone for another calibre in the financial climate of 1932 would certainly have killed the whole idea. As it was, the General's farsightedness was rewarded and the Garand was adopted in 1936. When the US went to war it was the only army to do so with its infantry largely armed with a self loading rifle, and it remained the only army so equipped throughout. In actual fact, the first battles of the Pacific War were fought with the old bolt action Springfield, as neither the regular army troops in the Philippines nor the Marine Corps had been issued with Garands, and indeed the Springfield lingered on until 1945, in rapidly dwindling numbers. But after 1943 all US combat troops carried the Garand and the very first time it was used in action the troops who had it were under General MacArthur's command. He did not miss the point, and quickly

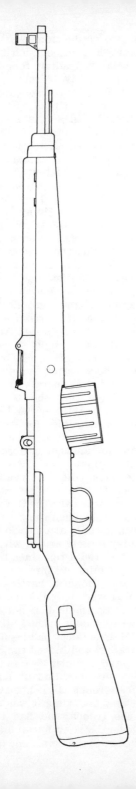

brought it out in his despatches. From that time onwards, the Garand was used in every theatre of war and proved itself to be a thoroughly reliable and serviceable weapon. General Patton went on record as saying that it was 'the best battle implement ever devised', and it earned similar praise in the Korean War. Even now it is still in service with many armies throughout the world.

The Garand, or M 1 to give it its proper title, was a simple and robust self loading rifle. The outline appearance is highly attractive as it is slim and well balanced, in fact it looks right, just as in the same way a properly designed railway locomotive looks right, and is obviously functional. The wooden stock runs to about half way up the barrel, and a wooden handguard covers the top and remaining front third. The last few inches of barrel are left exposed, and below it is the gas cylinder, which is almost the same length. The receiver is short, and the backsight mount above it. The action is deceptively simple. The short bolt is locked by two forward lugs which rotate and engage in recesses just behind the breech. Apart from these recesses the receiver is cut away so that the whole breech face and locking system can be easily cleaned, unlike the Mauser action where the locking recesses are hidden. The whole receiver is quite massive, although it takes little of the firing stresses, but as it is short the extra weight is less noticeable and it lends a degree of safety in the event of cartridge rupture or some similar catastrophe. The operating handle

**Model 43 Semi-Automatic Rifle (G43);** *Calibre:* **7.92 x 57mm;** *System of Operation:* **Gas: Semi-Automatic only;** *Length:* **44 inches;** *Barrel Length:* **21.62 inches;** *Feed Device:* **Detachable 10 Round, staggered row, box magazine;** *Sights: Front:* **Barleycorn;** *Rear:* **Tangent Leaf;** *Muzzle Velocity:* **Approx 2,550 feet per second;** *Weight:* **9.5 lbs**

Mauser KAR 98 K carbines on
the Italian front.

uns alongside the bolt, and rotates it
y a simple cam action. The operating
od which drives the handle to and
ro runs below the barrel when it
omes out of the gas cylinder, and it
hen picks up the return spring for the
olt, which accounts for the short re-
eiver as it has no return spring to
ccommodate. As the rod nears the
reech it bends away to the right and
gain upwards, to come out of the
rooden handguard and meet the
perating handle. Thus, every time
he rifle is fired there is a piece of
xposed metal moving backwards and
orwards along the right hand side at
considerable speed. If the firer has
ot been warned of this, or if he is
1ore than averagely stupid, it is
ossible to catch a finger between the
od and handguard but the accident is
1r less severe than it sounds, and the
sual result is just to stop the next
ound feeding into the chamber.
The most frequent criticism of the
arand is levelled at its magazine and
1ethod of loading. Here it does seem

that J Garand missed an opportunity,
and one wonders why. It is just possible that he was concerned about
weight, for the empty rifle weighs
$9\frac{1}{2}$lbs , or he may not have wished to
fit a vulnerable sheet metal box which
projected below the smooth outline
of the stock. Whatever the reason, he
was perhaps wrong, and it is a pity
that the US Army did not ask for the
magazine to be changed when they
accepted the weapon. Eight rounds
are held in an integral magazine
housed within the wooden stock. The
only method of loading is by charger
or clip, which holds the complete
eight rounds for one loading. The clip
is pressed down into the magazine and
remains there until empty, when it is
ejected. This is an unusual way of
doing it, and it was not universally
praised for various minor reasons,
one of which was the fact that a

85

magazine could not be 'topped up', it was a complete clip or nothing. Another small difficulty which appeared in action was a tendency to 'freeze' or stick when very wet. As the Pacific battle area was extremely wet for many months of the year, this could become an annoyance to the users, and it was only partly cured by using special lubricants.

A grenade launcher was produced, though not without some troubles, and it ingeniously allowed the gas cylinder to vent to the air when firing grenades, so preventing the mechanism from damage due to the higher pressures. When firing normal ball ammunition the gas vent closed, and the rifle worked in the usual way. A sniping version was issued, in which a telescope of 2.2 magnification was fitted to the receiver. An attempt was also made to produce a special short version, but this suffered the same fate as all the other ones had in Germany and Britain, and was soon discarded because it recoiled more, and had a larger muzzle blast and flash. In early 1944 a move was started to try and produce an automatic version of the Garand in order to replace the now rapidly ageing Browning Automatic Rifles. The design ran to a confusing number of models in the T series, from T 20 to T 22E2, but very few had been made by 1945, and none went into service. They all suffered from the usual defects of a rifle sized weapon which is expected to double as a light machine gun, and the idea was not followed up. When the war finished almost exactly 4,200,000 Garands had been made by two main contractors, of whom the Springfield Armory had produced the incredible total of 3,519,471, and the Winchester Repeating Arms Company the remainder. The Korean war gave another boost to manufacture, and brought the total up to 5,500,000, a record for a

**The .30 M 1903 Springfield rifle.**

*Above:* US sharpshooter armed with a Garand semi-automatic rifle in Italy
*Below:* US Marines using the .30 M1 rifle (Garand) against the Japanese

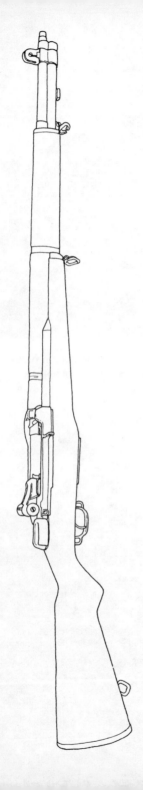

type which has survived throughout its life with no major modification and only very few minor ones. It had no vices, was highly reliable, and only required straightforward cleaning and oiling to keep it working for long periods. The most frequent mechanical failure was a broken firing pin, which was easily replaced.

With such a successful rifle as the Garand accepted into service as early as 1936 it is perhaps surprising that any other should even have been considered, much less used, but when war was declared in 1941 the army had some distance to go to equip all its units, and the Marine Corps were next in line after that, with the prospect of a lengthy wait. Both turned to the Johnson automatic rifle which they had seen and tried before the war and rejected. Designed and developed between 1936 and 1940 by Captain Melvin M Johnson, Jr, US Marine Corps Reserve, the Johnson was a highly original and interesting weapon. It worked by utilising the recoil of the barrel to operate the mechanism, and possessed other unique features also. The stock was very much of the straight line type though not so extreme as to demand high set sights. The barrel was unsupported for about half of its length thus giving a rather graceful and sporting air to the weapon, at the expense of a good deal of strength and the inability to fix a bayonet. A perforated sheet steel jacket formed a hand guard, but the *tour de force* of the whole gun was the magazine. This was a highly unusual rotary type which fitted beneath the receiver and

**M1 Rifle (Garand Semi-Automatic Rifle);** *Calibre:* **.30 US;** *System of Operation:* **Gas. Semi-Automatic;** *Length:* **43.6 inches;** *Barrel Length:* **24 inches;** *Feed System:* **8 Round. Staggered row. Non-detachable box magazine;** *Sights:* **Front: Blade with protecting ears.** *Rear:* **Aperture;** *Weight:* **9.5 lbs;** *Muzzle Velocity:* **2,805 feet per second**

*Above:* After D-Day a US paratrooper armed with an M1 rifle captures a German soldier. *Right:* A fragmentation grenade about to be launched

hardly altered the outline of the rifle at all. It held ten rounds and was loaded with single cartridges through a flap in the right hand side. The lips of the magazine were machined into the receiver, and so were never distorted nor damaged. The barrel could be easily dismounted, and this made it attractive for parachuting and some special operations, but the whole design was too unmilitary and liable to damage to be a success.

The Dutch government ordered and took delivery of a substantial number of Johnson rifles in 1941 and equipped its forces in the East Indies with them. Shortly afterwards the Japanese invaded and the orders ceased. The US Army and Marine Corps took up the remaining production, but the Johnson was never adopted as an official

US troops in Burma clean their M1s during their advance against the Japanese

weapon, and as supplies of the Garand came along it was dropped. Production of the dwindling numbers finally ended in the winter of 1943-44 and with it all development ceased also. In fact it had changed very little in that time, and really it was still a fundamentally sporting rifle which had strayed into the army. Unfortunately, the civilian demand for semi-automatic rifles is not large, and today the Johnson is a collector's item only. About 1,000 were chambered for 7mm Mauser ammunition, and sold to Chile, but there is no indication of how long they remained in service. None has survived.

The passing of the Johnson left the field clear for the Garand, which it held without challenge. During the rather critical early days of 1941 and '42 several thousand First World War Springfields were retained in service, and a few lasted afterwards as sniper

rifles, but by and large the US fought the war with one rifle only, and it must have been a continual blessing to the supply and repair echelons that she did so.

The Russian picture is in some contrast to that of the American, as at least four different rifles were in service at one time or another during the war, and very probably all were in use at the same time at one period. Luckily they all used the same ammunition. The basic Soviet rifle was the Moissin-Nagant, a bolt action five shot magazine repeater which first entered service in the Czar's army in 1891. It shared with the Italian Mannlicher-Carcano the distinction of being one of the oldest designs to be used by the combatants on either side, and in some ways it was a typically Russian weapon. There is little that is remarkable about the Moissin-Nagant, it is a simple weapon, although the bolt has been criticised for being in two pieces, and so more complicated than it need be, but the rest of it is quite straightforward. Until 1930 the sights were graduated in *arshins*, which is an archaic Russian measurement of distance, and the calibre was quoted in *lines*, a *line* being roughly equal to one-tenth of an inch. But the Soviet government swept away these quaint relics and substituted the metric system so that the calibre became 7.62mm, and the sights were graduated in metres – with incidentally, a better backsight. This new rifle was called the model 1891/30, and together with a carbine version introduced in 1938 it lasted right through as the standard infantry weapon until 1950. The best known use of it is as a sniper rifle, as the Soviet propaganda went to some lengths to glamourize their snipers. For this task the rifle was fitted with a 4-power or sometimes a 3.5-power telescope similar to a civilian hunting 'scope, and the bolt handle was turned down to fit flush alongside the body. It was a perfectly accurate weapon for this role, but it also equipped the greater majority of the infantry as well. The carbine was given to service units and vehicle crews, and it had one difference from the rifle apart from the shorter barrel, in that a bayonet could not be fixed, but this was corrected in the 1944 model when a folding bayonet was fixed on. Folding bayonets are a largely Russian device in modern times, though they were also used in Italy and Japan to a limited extent.

The old Moissin-Nagant gained a good reputation for reliability in all conditions, but it was obviously obsolete, or at least obsolescent, long before the war even started. Attempts were therefore made to produce a proper self loading rifle, and the initial designs began at the same time as the Garand story, that is in the early 1930s. A Tokarev design of 1932 was replaced by a Simonov in 1936, and again by a Tokarev in 1938. Each was an improvement on the other, and the 1936 Simonov was made in some quantities, though not enough

to make it a significant addition to the infantry armoury. The Tokarev model 38 was, however, put into volume production and used in action in the Finnish war of 1939/40. The Finns captured large numbers of Tokarevs and after the war were astute enough to sell them to arms collectors as curios, thereby reaping a little profit! It was a gas operated rifle of conventional appearance, not unlike a Garand, but with a different locking system, and an unusual chamber in which flutes were cut to help the cartridge extract. As the round fired, gas was allowed to leak round the case via the flutes, and support the outside of the case so that it in effect 'floated' in the chamber. This prevented it from sticking to the chamber walls and giving hard extraction. The idea was not original, but it is not usually met with as it points to a fundamental failure in the design somewhere, and in the case of the Tokarev it was in the ammunition.

The old 1908 7.62mm rimmed round was not well suited to the light Tokarev rifle, and it gave continual feed troubles. Another factor which counted against the Tokarev was its lack of robustness. Great efforts had been made in the design to keep the weight down to that of the bolt action rifle, and in the process some strength was lost. It was also not an easy rifle to strip, particularly under winter conditions and it suffered from insufficient power in the gas system. An improved model in 1940 went some way to curing these faults, but not far enough, and it is reported that manufacture ceased in 1944. By that time many thousands had been made and used, although it never completely replaced the Moissin-Nagant in any units. Once again sniping was a way of publicising the rifle, but how often it was so used one cannot tell. A small bayonet was specially made for the Tokarev and in 1940 a selective fire version was made in small numbers. Very few seem to have been used. The Italian army has already been

mentioned as possessing one of the older rifles in the war, and not only was it old, it was also one of the worst. Quite why Mussolini did nothing to change it will never be known, but perhaps he found road building and keeping the trains on time were difficult enough for one man. Whatever the reason, the model 1891 Mannlicher-Carcano was well outdated by 1918, and by 1938 it was near to the bottom of the European league. In its original concept it was sound enough, for it used a light bullet and low chamber pressures to give a light rifle with low recoil, but yet retained a reasonable range. The calibre was 6.5mm and the bullet had a rounded nose, with a moderately high muzzle velocity. But the ballistics were bad, and the bullet quickly lost velocity down range. A Mauser type bolt was used, and the receiver was kept low in weight by machining off all unnecessary metal. This has given the rifle a reputation for being weak and dangerous, which it by no means merits if used with the ammunition intended for it. However, to get back to the story, in 1938 it was decided to uprate the performance by using another bullet of greater calibre namely 7.35mm, and, of course, a new cartridge case and so a new barrel. It was intended that the chamber pressures should be the same as for the 6.5mm, but that this larger calibre bullet should, in fact, be lighter – achieved by giving it a long pointed nose, and so it would be faster at the muzzle. Finally, the bullet had an aluminium nose section which meant that it became unstable when it hit anything and began to tumble. It was reckoned that this feature was highly desirable as it would give far more unpleasant wounds when it hit a man. Uplifted by these kindly thoughts the Italians went into production.

Having got nicely under way with the new design, the Italian government

decided that it could not afford to put enough money into the project to ensure that all rifles were converted by the time the war came, and so those that had been changed were changed back again, and the army remained at 6.5mm! In fact, not every one was changed back to 6.5mm, and throughout the war there were several thousand useless 7.5mm weapons sitting in store doing nothing at all, only to be sold after the war as curios. The resulting rifle from these Alice in Wonderland contortions was the model 1938 carbine, which achieved lasting notoriety by being the weapon which shot President Kennedy, thereby proving that it was neither entirely harmless nor inaccurate. This carbine weighed 6.5lbs, making it the lightest rifle of any Second World War combatant, and had one or two odd features. It was loaded with a 6-round clip which remained in the magazine until all the rounds were fired, when it fell out through a large hole in the bottom, as with all Mannlicher designs. The same hole acted also as a convenient scoop for the collection of mud and sand. The backsight was a fixed vee notch, offering no alteration for range or windage, scarcely an encouragement to open fire at any but point blank range, and finally, the rifling had a progressive twist, winding tighter towards the muzzle.

Quite a neat knife bayonet came with the carbine, and for some unhappy users there was a grenade launcher. Of all the optional extras that have ever been offered for rifles this one must surely take the all time prize for being the most awkward and clumsy. It was a separate barrel and breech, quite robustly made, which was mounted on the right hand of the carbine. A ballistic cartridge was used to fire the grenade out of the barrel, and the breech was sealed by taking the bolt out of the carbine, and fitting it into the launcher. By and large this system has never been beaten for combining the worst of all possible cases. The carbine is unbalanced by the load on

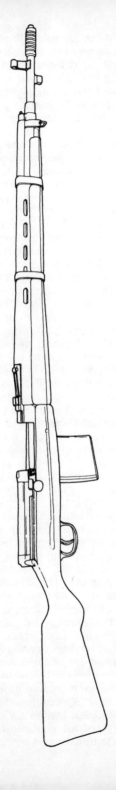

one side, its weight is excessive, and while firing the grenade launcher the unfortunate rifleman is defenceless. Even a dextrous man must have taken a considerable time to bring this contraption into action, and it would take an absolute Houdini to cope with it in a fast moving infantry battle. In a way it typifies the Italian prewar approach to weapons, and leaves one sympathising with their soldiers.

The same mentality produced a little infantry mortar that has so many gadgets on it that it weighs over 30lbs. It folds up into a pack with a pad to go against the carrier's back, and unfolds to a complicated shape on which the firer sits rather like a man on a rowing machine. By moving a lever backwards and forwards the breech is opened and closed, and the second man of the team pops a bomb in as the opportunity is offered. Propelling cartridges are self loaded by the lever action, and there is an ingenious arrangement for altering the muzzle velocity for different ranges which is a combination of two known unsuccessful systems. The end product of all this physical and mechanical effort is to throw a bomb weighing less than 1lb to a range of less than 500 yards. All in all, the business of projecting explosive munitions from infantry launchers was not one in which the Italians can be said to have led the field. But we digress once again.

The carbine was not the only rifle issued; there were many long 6.5mm rifles also, and even a few ancient Mannlichers dating from the First World War, which took 8mm ammunition, and cannot have eased the supply

**M38 Tokarev Semi-Automatic Rifle;** *Calibre:* 7.62; *System of Operation:* Gas. Semi-Automatic; *Length:* 48.1 inches; *Barrel length:* 25 inches; *Sights. Front:* Hooded post; *Sights. Rear:* Tangent; *Weight:* 8.70 pounds; *Magazine Capacity:* 10 rounds; *Rate of Fire:* 25 rounds per minute

*Above:* Soviet Marines equipped with PPSh M 1941 sub-machine guns and Tokarev semi-automatic rifles. *Below:* The 7.92mm Mannlicher Carcano rifle dating from 1891 was obselescent at the outbreak of the war

problem. There was also a small number of semi-automatic rifles in service, though only to specialist troops. The best one was the Breda Model 1935, which fired the 6.5mm round and worked by gas action. It was expensive to make, and the finance was never forthcoming to develop it. This is a pity as it could have become a useful forerunner of the assault rifle if it had been followed up. In this role the 6.5mm round may have had something to offer.

We must now leave the Italian weapons and pass on to those of the Japanese. As we have already seen, there is always a good deal of confusion in the Type classification of Japanese equipments, so it may be as well to try and take a simple look at the field before

delving into any detail. There were two calibres of ammunition for rifles, with three types of rifles firing one, and four types the other. So, seven different types or marks of weapon, and two different types of ammunition. The calibres were 6.5mm and 7.7mm. The 6.5mm dated from 1897, and had already fought two major wars by 1941, quite apart from two or three minor ones. It suffered from the same disadvantages as the Italian 6.5mm though it should be noted that the two are not by any means the same round, and it was being replaced by the 7.7mm in 1939. The rifles which fired the 6.5mm were derived from a 1905 design, which in the Japanese nomenclature was the Type 38 Arisaka.

**The Japanese 6.5mm type 38 rifle in action in Shanghai**

This was a straight copy of the Mauser, recalibred to 6.5mm, and indeed the rifle does look quite similar to the Gar 98. It came in four sizes, a Type 38 rifle and carbine, a Type 44 carbine,

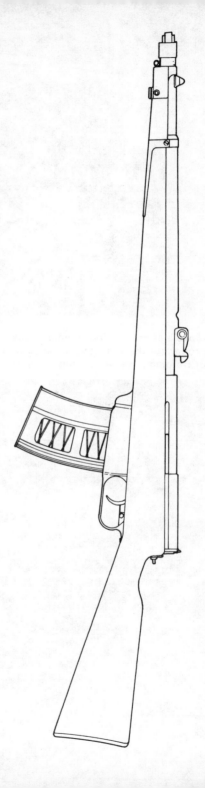

Italian Breda 35 Semi-Automatic Rifle; *calibre:* 6.5m. Developed for export in .92mm and 7.62mm calibres. Later standardised to 7.35mm; *System of operation:* Gas. Semi-Automatic/selective.

*Above and below:* The standard Japanese rifle, the 6.5mm Type 38 Arisaka, throughout the war. It was also used in vast numbers by many western nations for training purposes during the Second World War

and a Type 97 rifle.

The Type 38 rifle and carbine are no more than the Mauser copies already mentioned. Both fought throughout the war, and were the major infantry weapons. The magazine held five rounds, and the bayonet was a long, sword type, already by 1939 well out of date. The Type 44 was a 1911 cavalry version fitted with a folding bayonet, and the Type 97 was a sniping variant of the long rifle. It had a wire monopod attached to the upper barrel band, presumably as an aid to steadier shooting but it seems to be far too long for anyone but a giant to use with comfort. Naturally, there was a telescopic sight. The Type 38s fitted two kinds of grenade launcher, both faithful copies of the German ones. Unusually, the propellant was in a round of ammunition with a wooden bullet which broke up on hitting the grenade. Why a wooden bullet is hard to see because it would be so easy to confuse it with ball rounds in the heat of combat, and so give rise to some trouble. But it gave the Allied propagandists a field day when some were captured, and were used to show how desperate were the shortages in Japan that the army even had to fire wooden bullets! The genuine round gave a very small flash and recoil, so that in the jungle of Burma and on the Pacific island campaigns it was often hard to decide where a shot had come from. The Japanese were also adept at using snipers, or more properly sharpshooters, and the Ariska was ideal for work of this kind.

Although the 7.7mm rifles were basically the same as the 6.5mm, the process of replacing went along very slowly, and was not by any means complete by 1945. The task was just too much for Japanese industry in the middle of a war. The Type 99 as it was known, started to come into service in 1941, and there were three variants, a long, a short, and a collapsible. The first two are self-explanatory, the last is a Japanese peculiarity. The rifle was a short version, and it took down into two parts, splitting at a point just in front of the receiver. The barrel unscrewed from the breech, and the wooden stock unpinned. The early models unscrewed their barrels as they fired, so a later modification was to pin it in place also. This enthusiasm for dismantling was apparently prompted by the paratroops, and it led to other rifles being made with a hinge at the small of the butt, a dreadful botch of a job. Apart from these anomalies, the Japanese rifles were not too bad, and the Type 38 was made in enormous quantities during its long life, as many as 10,000,000 has been quoted as the total output, but this is only a guess as there are no records left. After 1943 the standard drops noticeably, and some of the weapons produced in the last years of the war are downright bad. The finish is poor, the metal below specification, the sights simplified to a single peep aperture, and the wooden handguards cut down. Despite experimenting with semi-automatic rifles since 1922, none were produced during the Second World War, and the infantry fought with bolt actions throughout.

One of the fascinations of the study of small arms, and those of the Second World War are no exception, is to see how long certain types remain in service. We have mentioned the elderly models used by Russia and Italy, but France takes pride of place for longevity with the 1886 Lebel. This remarkable antique was actually the first ever military rifle in the world to use smokeless powder, and it was still in limited service in the French army in 1939. It was a long heavy weapon, and the magazine was tubular, running forward from the breech under the barrel. It fired an obsolete 8mm round which had an awkward cartridge case with a large rimmed base. It is highly doubtful if any actual 1886 rifles remained in use in 1939, but there were many thousands built to the same specification left from the First World War. These were the ones which saw service until the German invasion, and there is some evidence that the

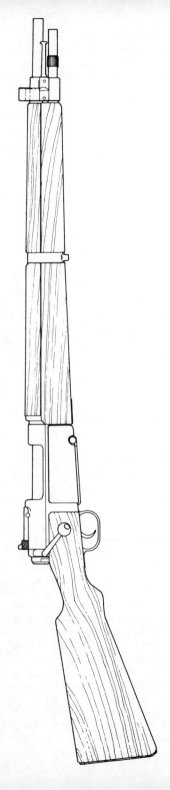

occupying forces took over certain stocks and armed reserve units with them. In the end the Lebel must have served in European armies for almost sixty years, but even this is not quite a record as the Enfield family survived in the British army for well over sixty-five. In addition to the Lebel the French army started the war with large numbers of the Berthier rifle and carbine. Infantry carried the rifle, service units the carbine. The Berthier was an 1890 model of rather uninspired design, modified to 7.5mm from 8mm in the late 1930s. The Berthier retained the clumsy Lebel bolt, which did not lend itself to rapid fire, and until 1935 it still had its original Mannlicher type magazine. After that date the loading was changed to a Mauser style of magazine. There is little that is attractive about the Berthier and probably its best epitaph is to say that it was strong and serviceable.

The French were well aware that their army was equipped with museum pieces, and work was started soon after the First World War to modernize them. Unfortunately, money was scarcer in France than anywhere else and the programme went abysmally slowly. The 7.5mm round appeared in 1924, and a new rifle in 1932; this was the MAS Model 32, followed later by the Model 36 which was the one selected for production. It was the last bolt action rifle to be designed for military use, an almost incredible anachronism as manufacture started at the same time as the Garand production in the USA, and it was simple in the extreme. It was also ugly. The bolt was of large diameter, like the Lebel

**MAS 1936 Rifle;** *Calibre:* **7.5mm;** *Length:* **40.13 inches;** *Barrel Length:* **17.7 inches;** *Feed Device:* **5 Round integral staggered row, box magazine;** *Sights:* **Front: Barleycorn with Guards; Rear: Ramp with aperture;** *Muzzle Velocity:* **2,700 feet per second Weight 8.29 lbs**

And the bolt handle is at the back of it that it has to be bent forward to ing it to a convenient place for the er's hand. The stock was in two eces, again like the Lebel, and the agazine only held five rounds. A ort barrelled version was made for ratroops, and it had a hollow folding uminium butt stock. Finally, the AS inherited one of the incredible atures of both Level and Berthier – ere was no safety catch. The only y to carry any of these rifles in fety when they were loaded was to se the bolt on to an empty breech. ace a round was chambered the wea- n was highly dangerous. Like the rthier and Lebel, it was used by the rman occupying troops, and after e war returned into French service til 1949. A few were seen in the hands the police in the 1968 student riots.

**The MAS 36, the last manually operated bolt action rifle to be produced in large numbers by any major power**

And it is on this sober note that the survey of rifles must end. The field was wide enough; and in some ways it has mirrored the national characteristics of the countries who figured in it. The industry and invention of the Ger- mans, the single-minded mass produc- tion of the Americans, the conserva- tism of the British, the pragmatic ap- proach of the Russians, and the French – at least in their rifles – looking backward rather than for- ward. All these showed clearly enough – which may start another field for psychologists to follow, what about fusilology, the art or science of de- ducing a nation's habits from its infantry weapons?

# Assault rifles

The standard bolt action rifles of the First World War showed up badly in the trench fighting. They were too big, too heavy, too powerful, and they did not fire automatically. The machine gun dominated the battle, and the individual rifle man didn't stand a chance against it. Since the trenches were only a few yards apart it soon became clear that a smaller rifle able to fire automatic when required and firing a less powerful cartridge would do just as well as the existing one and be far handier to use. The idea was put forward on both sides of the lines, but it got no further than being an idea. By the time it was realised what was needed, and by the time the ideas had reached the proper quarters, the war was well on into its second year with arms production in full swing all over Europe. Patterns were standardized, and no country was going to risk stopping it all to start on a fresh range of weapons and ammunition. The daily consumption of small arms cartridges was measured in tons, and the munitions factories only just kept up with it. It was a delicate balance, and it would not tolerate any monkeying about. So the ideas had to go on ice, and a little effort was put into submachine guns, which was not quite what the originators meant. However, the seed had been sown, and it stayed in the minds of some German officers.

Their project very closely resembled what is now accepted as the classic definition of an assault rifle; that is a rifle in which the characteristics are light weight, simplicity of design reasonably large magazine capacity and the capability of firing either single shot or automatic. It is a convenient term because the weapon which fulfils these requirements is automatically separated from the conventional bolt action rifles, the light machine guns, and the semi-automatic infantry rifles. The Germans coined the descriptive name 'assault rifle' for their new weapon in 1944, and it is now th generally accepted term in many languages. The intention behind an assault rifle is that it shall be able to fulfil three different tactical uses. First it must act as a sub-machine gun; in other words it must be light, handy and capable of automatic fire without excessive recoil or muzzle movement. Second, it must be a semi-automatic rifle for use in normal infantry fighting at the sort of ranges encountered on a battlefield. It therefore needs to be able to shoot accurately to at least 400 yards, and to deliver a bullet which still has a good punch at that distance. Third, it must be able to operate as the light-fire support weapon of the squad or group, and this calls for the ability to deliver automatic fire with reasonable accuracy and consistency out to at least 400 yards, if not further, and to have a sufficiently large magazine to enable the firer to get off several bursts without having to reload. One can sympathise with the military staffs who rejected this specification in the interwar years, for it needed more than a clever design to make work. What was needed was a completely new approach to the problem of the infantryman's weapon, and not just a rehash of existing models.

The only way to a successful design lay first of all through the ammunition, and this had been realised for some time, though not in the context of producing an assault rifle. The brass cased cartridge loaded with smokeless powder, firing a nickel jacketed bullet had appeared in the 1880s in a roughly similar shape in nearly all the countries in the world. The calibre w

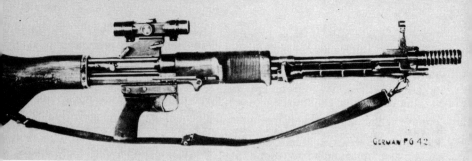

The 7.92mm Fallschirmjäger Gewehr 42, the Parachutist's Rifle. Wooden stock, telescopic sights, bi-pod folded

early the same also, at about .30-inch, r 7.65mm, and by the first decade of he 20th Century it was quite difficult o tell one country's ammunition from nother's without a close examination. ll were effective to at least 1,000 ards, and usually more than that. In 909 the Small Arms Committee of the ritish Ordnance Board realised that mmunition of this type was too pow-ful for normal infantry battle use, ad after some deliberation they re-ommended a reduction in calibre to out .25-inch, with a consequent re-action in the size and weight of the eapon which fired it, and a slight loss maximum range. This, it was con-dered, could well be sacrificed. othing came of the idea, and in 1916 a oposal was put to the German ord-ance office suggesting that 400 metres as sufficient range for an infantry fle, and that this could be achieved th a lower powered rifle cartridge of naller calibre. This was no more ccessful. Finally, in the USA during e 1920s, a designer called Pedersen oduced a semi-automatic rifle of 6-inch calibre which was quite suc-ssful, but the Chief of Staff ruled it t and ordered that any automatic le must fire the .30 calibre round al-ady existing.

It was simply that every country d too much capital invested in exis-ag equipment and ammunition. No ubt, given a clean sheet any one of em would have gone straight for me sort of assault rifle, but in the 20s and 30s there were precious few an sheets to be found anywhere, d not much hint of any in the future her. Versailles had ensured eternal

**The 7.92mm Fallschirmjäger Gewehr 42, the Parachutist's Rifle. Wooden stock, telescopic sights, bi-pod folded**

peace in Europe, so what point in making new weapons? Even the de-signers slept, and when Europe started to rearm there was no time left to start the cycle of drawing board, pro-totype and tooling up for production. All was rush and haste, and the well proved models were made again. Only in Germany was a small body of mili-tary officers sufficiently far sighted not to be panicked by the atmosphere, and to take a chance to put their ideas into practice. But their story comes a little later, we must digress for a mo-ment to paint in the background.

The true history of the emergence of the assault rifle is purely German, but there was one early oddity which, had it survived, would probably have been accepted as the first one of the breed. Strangely, it was in Russia, a country which, despite its claims, has never been very prominent in the design of small arms. In 1916 the well known Russian designer, Federov, produced an automatic rifle which he called the Automat. It had the ability to fire automatic or single shot, was fairly light, was effective to normal infantry fighting ranges, and had a reasonable magazine capacity. It was evolved from several previous models of semi-automatic rifle, none of which had been produced in more than very small numbers. The significant point of the Automat was that it used a relatively low powered round which was already in service in the Imperial Russian Army. This was the 6.5mm Japanese rifle cartridge, which had been adopted in Russia in limited numbers after the war of 1905. It was only low powered in the sense that it fired a smaller and lighter bullet than its contemporaries in other countries, and for this reason was unpopular in Russia, but it suited Federov ideally as it permitted a reasonably light weapon to be made. By using a service round he overcame the usual initial hurdle that was defeating all other designers, and the Automat was produced in small numbers for the Red Army after the Revolution. It was quickly superseded, one reason being that the 6.5mm round was dropped. This was a pity, for it was a businesslike weapon, with a wooden stock, a forward pistol grip, and a modern looking curved box magazine underneath. The weight was roughly 9½lbs, and the rate of fire 600 shots per minute. The system of operation was novel as it used the recoil of the barrel to unlock the breech, and the idea has not been copied since there are certain technical disadvantages to it. However, it was a striking design and deserved a better fate.

There were other Russian assault rifles in production in very small quantities in the 1920s and 1930s, notably those by Tokarev, but only one or two of these were true assault rifles, and they all suffered from the fundamental drawback that they fired the full powered cartridge of the Soviet forces. The selective fire capability seems to have been dropped by the start of the 1941 war with Hitler's Germany, and there are no records known of any actual battle use of the rifles as assault rifles, most were converted and used as semi-automatic rifles by snipers.

In Germany, the traditional approach to infantry weapons was as strong as in any other country, and the First World War exerted a powerful influence over most official thinking. A certain amount of work went on in secrecy in the 1920s and 30s both inside and outside Germany, but although the targets set were imaginative and sensible, not much progress had been made in producing new weapons by the time that it had become imperative to rearm. The ideas of 1918 still controlled weapon development and the infantry weapons which were produced in the rearmament phase of the early and mid 1930s were all elderly and familiar in pattern. However, a small section of the German weapon procurement staff was thinking ahead and they quietly went about specifying a new cartridge of lower power This was followed by a further development to a multi-purpose infantry weapon, with all the characteristics of the assault rifle. Having settled on what was wanted, little further time was lost in discussing it. It was quite apparent that no existing cartridge would fulfil all that they needed, and so contracts were immediately placed for its design. A firm was selected to undertake it, and another firm set about designing the weapon.

It was now 1938 and the Germans were aware that they had very little time in which to produce their new rifle if it was to be of any use in the war which was now only just around the corner, so they adopted the novel idea of developing cartridge and weapon at the same time to speed it up. While at first sight this seems to be a potentially disastrous course, it is feasible both sides go to great lengths to keep each other informed. The cartridge contract went to the firm of Polte, and the weapon to Haenel, both being in the same area of Germany. Fifty prototypes of the rifle were required by 1942, and great insistence was laid on ease of manufacture of the finished design. The cartridge produced by Polte was excellent in every way, and gave rise to a long line of similar ones which are in service today, and this despite the fact that it was designed and produced in about two years, or very little more. Fate is not usually kind to people who take liberties with time, as we have seen before in the small arms story.

The design of this cartridge had

be done in short order, and this virtually eliminated any hope of going to some radically new idea; in addition, there was neither time nor finance to make new dies and gauges for the factories. In the end the designing was virtually all done on the workshop floor, trying out the ideas in metal as they were thought of. The result was the 'Kurz', or short, round of the same calibre as the existing rifle, that is 7.92mm. Both the case and the bullet were shortened but the circular dimensions were retained. This meant that the most value could be obtained from the existing tools and gauges, and the fewest possible new ones had to be made up. It was a brilliant compromise and it worked. By using the older diameters in the now shorter case, the slope of the cartridge wall was steeper, in other words the case was more nearly conical in shape. This is a good point for most automatic weapons as it allows the case to be positioned in the breech with some precision, and thus accurately placed for the firing pin to hit it. Later, as the story will tell, there came about a blowback version of the rifle, and the steeply sloping case walls were an embarrassment in this version, and required the chamber to be fluted to allow gas to flow round the outside of the case and equalize the pressure. The complete round weighed two-thirds of the full size one, and fired its lighter bullet at 2,300 feet per second, which was enough to give it quite adequate performance out to 400 metres. The cases were apparently all made of steel which in itself was an innovation, and lacquered to prevent rust. They have a distinctive brown colour, quite unlike brass.

The story here becomes more complicated, because some time in 1940 the firm of Walther, an experienced gun manufactory, entered the field, and was allowed to make its own design. It seems, however, that certain restrictions were placed on them, possibly in the magazine which had already been produced by Haenel, and which had to

MKb 42 (H) Assault Rifle; *Calibre:* 7.92mm Kurz; *System of Operation:* Gas. Selective fire; *Length:* 37 inches; *Barrel Length:* 14.37 inches; *Feed Device:* Detachable 30 Round, staggered row, box magazine; *Sights: Front:* Hooded Barleycorn; *Rear:* Tangent with U notch; *Muzzle Velocity:* Approx 2,100 feet per second; *Cyclic Rate:* 500 rounds per minute; *Weight:* 11.06 lbs

be common to both models. Haenel was no newcomer to gun making, and the chief designer was Hugo Schmeisser, who drew on his earlier experience and knowledge in laying out the Haenel weapon. The first prototype may have been made in late 1941, and by this time the HKW had directed a firm of steel stamping specialists to assist in the designing so that final production could start without too much delay. There was undoubted wisdom in this, for Haenel and Schmeisser were gun makers of the old school, and conditioned to thinking in terms of weapons intended for a long life, and not to worry too much about the cost and time taken to manufacture. There were clashes right away, but none so serious as to hold up the work, and all fifty prototypes were ready on time in mid 1942.

Four years is a remarkably short time in which to produce an entirely new weapon and its ammunition, and much credit must go to the men who did it. Later on in the war there were several occasions in which weapons were produced in a shorter time than this, but these were usually only derivations of existing designs, and the development cycle could be shorter as a result. However, the fifty duly appeared, and thirty-five were sent off immediately for trial in the hands of troops. At the same time plans were made for large scale production, though it must be taken that such plans had started some time before, and were already well advanced, because Haenel was required to produce the first batch in three months from the prototype date. Haenel did go to production, and altogether probably 10,000 were made, work finishing in 1943. These guns were known as MKb 42, followed by an (H) to signify Haenel.

Walther produced their prototype at roughly the same moment as Haenel, and went to production on what was called the MKb 42 (W). Both designs were similar in that they were practical, easily handled rifles, with a straight line to the top of the stock and receiver, and the fore end of the stock made of metal. The sloping pistol grip had plastic grips, the sights stood on top of blocks on the barrel and receiver, and the small butt stock was made of wood. A curved magazine fed upwards into the receiver, and held thirty rounds. A bayonet lug was fitted and the muzzle had to accept a grenade launcher. Steel stampings were used extensively, and the general impression one gets on handling either of the designs is that it is a tough, realistic, and sensible weapon, with no nonsense in its conception.

An early opportunity was provided to try out the first production models when in 1942 an infantry unit known by the name of 'Kampfgruppe Scherer' was isolated on the Eastern Front. A supply of MKs was dropped to them by parachute and the gruppe fought their way back to the main front. After this the rifle's reputation was made, and there were loud demands for it to be issued to all infantry. There is no doubt that the German ordnance would have acceded to this and gone into large scale production, had not Hitler intervened and stopped them. There are so many stories about Hitler and his interference in the German arms development that it is now quite impossible to tell truth from fiction. Since truth is likely to be the more stupid and unlikely tale, one way of doing it is to believe the crazier version. By applying this rule it soon becomes apparent that he was the best general the Allies had. In the case of MK 43 he is said to have drawn on his experience in the First World War to condemn it because it had insufficient range (where was Corporal Hitler if he needed more than 400 yards?), and also because there were millions of rounds of 7.92mm long rounds in stock. So there were, but they would have been used up by the time MK 43 came into service in large numbers, but he had his way, and stopped production.

The ordnance officers were in a difficult position. They knew that they had a winner, but they were not allowed to make it. It had been proved in battle, but the Head of State had condemned it. Factory effort was not to be allocated to it, yet they had two factories tooled up ready for it, and more standing by. One can hardly blame them for doing what generations of officers have done when given a stupid order by a superior. They saluted and carried on doing what they had been told to stop. They were not quite so silly as to do it openly, but the Wehrmacht protected them somehow within the German war machine, and as a cover the name was changed to MP 43, making it look as if machine pistols were being made. They must have been brave men who decided on this course, for Hitler was not pleasant when disobeyed, but manufacture continued, and in 1943 the Walther model was dropped. From then on the Haenel rifle was known as the MP 43. It was demonstrated to Hitler for a second time in 1943 and again rejected. Again some work continued and small numbers were made and used on the Eastern Front. Quite how many were produced in this period is not known, but a figure of 14,000 total at the end of 1943 has been quoted, which is tiny when compared with normal small arms production runs. Some time in the latter end of 1943 Hitler was in conversation with some divisional commanders from the Russian front, and all asked him for the same thing, namely more MP 43s. He was furious to learn that his forbidden weapon was in service and demanded an inquiry. The results were so favourable that he completely changed his view and ordered priority production to begin straight away. The men who had defied him were now justified, and it is to be hoped that they gained some credit for it, but too much time had been lost and production never caught up with demand, despite the use of extensive sub-contracting both for making the parts and assembling the final product. It was a minor miracle that any production could be undertaken at all, for if Hitler's original

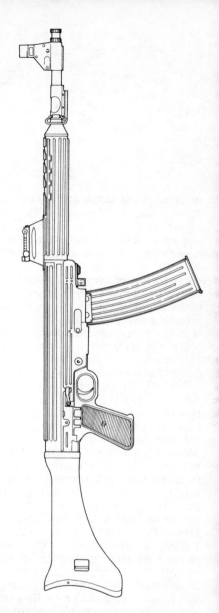

MKb 42 (W) Assault Rifle; *Calibre:* 7.92mm Kurz; System of Operation: Gas. Selective fire; *Length:* 36.75 inches; *Barrel Length:* 16.1 inches; *Feed Device:* Detachable 30 Round, staggered row, box magazine; *Sights: Front:* Hooded Barleycorn; *Rear:* Tangent with U notch; *Muzzle Velocity:* 2,132 feet per second; *Cyclic Rate:* 600 rounds per minute; *Weight:* 9.75 lbs

107

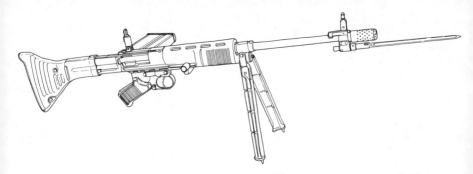

**Paratroop Rifle Model 42 –** *Fallschirmjäger Gewehr* (FG 42); *Calibre:* 7.92 x 57mm; *System of Operation:* Gas. Selective fire; *Length:* 37 inches; *Barrel Length:* 19.75 inches; *Feed Device:* Detachable 20 Round, staggered row, box magazine; *Sights: Front:* Barleycorn on Folding Base; *Rear:* Aperture on Folding Base; *Muzzle Velocity:* Approx 2,500 feet per second; *Weight:* 9.93 lbs

order had been obeyed it would have been quite impossible to start manufacturing from the beginning without a further delay of at least two years. But the tools and jigs were still in being, the factories laid out, and the experience to hand. Yet the final quantities in service in 1945 were small.

One novelty in the MP 43 was this decentralised production system. In theory it seems simple to send drawings out to factories all over the country and have them make the parts which are then sent to other centres for assembly. In Germany, suffering from continuous strategic bombing attacks, the attractions were obvious, but the drawbacks were often immense and not easily overcome. The greatest difficulty is to ensure that all the sub-contractors are making exactly the same thing in exactly the same way. If they aren't the final assembly is unsatisfactory and much time is lost in reworking the parts. By having so many fingers in the pie it is not easy to lay the blame for failings in the right quarter, and the source of the trouble may go untraced for a long time. Finally, if the country is being steadily bombed as Germany was, the sheer business of transport becomes a burden. All these troubles afflicted the MP 43, and they had by no means been solved when the war ended. Given more time they might have been, but,

luckily for the Allies, time was heavily against the Reich after 1943.

In 1944, the name was changed to MP 44 although no significant alterations were made to the design, but now that the MP 44 was accepted and in service other designers became quite active in producing their own, firing the Kurz round. One of these was a Mauser model which used a delayed blowback system of operation, and offered a considerable saving in weight. While it came too late for the war, it was continued in Spain after 1945 and became the CETME, and later returned to Germany as the present G 3 firing the NATO ammunition. A little later in 1944 the MP 44 assumed the name of 'Sturmgewehr 44', its final and best known title. The nearest translation of *Sturmgewehr* is 'Assault Rifle', and so, at last, the name and the weapon were matched.

The choice was almost certainly influenced by propaganda as much as any tactical use, for although assault rifles were ideal for delivering decisive short range full automatic fire during the final stages of infantry assault, by 1944 the German army was not making many such assaults. The general movement on the Eastern Front was backwards, and the same is true of the fighting in France and the Low Countries. The infantry used it as a general purpose rifle, and made no attempt to replace the machine gun already in the squad. The result of introducing the *Sturmgewehr* into an infantry squad was vastly to increase its firepower, and so make it a far more devastating and effective unit. Priority was given to the Eastern Front, where the pressures were greater, and only relatively small numbers were met by British and American troops. As usual when some new weapon is encountered, its performance tends to be overrated, but in this case the reports were perhaps nearer the truth than they normally were. Some idea of the relatively small numbers of *Sturmgewehr* in use in the German army may be gained from the fact that as late as May 1943 the US Intelligence Handbook describing enemy weapons makes no mention of it, nor its ammunition.

However, MP 43, or *Sturmgewehr* 44, was not the only assault rifle designed and produced in Germany during the Second World War. There was one other which comes into the classification, and which also saw service. Like the *Sturmgewehr*, its acceptance and introduction were not without heartbreaks, reverses and subterfuge, but by and large it had an easier passage due to its sponsors, for it was a Luftwaffe weapon. In Germany the parachute troops came under the control of the Luftwaffe, a fact which they used to great advantage whenever they wanted something for ground fighting, which the army either did not have, or did not approve of. The parachutists simply went back to the Luftwaffe and ordered it through them, and in doing this they had the benevolent backing of the Marshal of Luftwaffe, Hermann Göring himself. To him the parachutists were his personal army, and he was quite prepared to indulge them to any extent that they wanted. In the case of the rifle, the Luftwaffe watched the early development of the *Sturmgewehr*, and decided against adopting it, largely on account of the shorter range of the round. They felt that they needed the same characteristics, but using the full powered round already standardized for infantry, and apart from this one alteration, their specification reads almost word for word with the *Sturmgewehr*. At first the army was asked to develop it, but it was turned down, and the Luftwaffe launched out on its own.

The decision was taken to go ahead

**The Parachutist's Rifle (FG 42), with plastic butt and bayonet fitted. First used in the raid to free Mussolini**

A paratrooper of the German 1st Parachute Division uses the FG 42 in the Battle of Cassino

with the final draft of the specification early in 1940, and one firm who took up the contract was Rheinmetall. The first prototype was ready in 1942, only eighteen months later, an incredibly short space of time, but it must be remembered that they were using ammunition which already existed, and with which they were very familiar. Another reason is the paratroop assault on Crete. As a result of this very expensive action, the Luftwaffe became convinced, quite rightly in retrospect, that paratroops urgently needed a selective fire weapon, and more pressure was put on the firms designing it. The troops who fought in Crete were equally clear that the weapon they wanted had to have a long range, and so this part of the specification became firmly and immovably written in. In one respect the Germans were correct to do this, because experience in battle should never be lightly thrown away, but what prompted it is not now so clear as it was in 1941. An examination of the Crete battles shows that on some occasions the assaulting glider-borne and paratroop forces were pinned down by long range small arms fire from the defenders, but by and large the infantry actions were fought out at the more normal ranges of less than 400 yards, and any longer range firing was given to mortars and the few machine guns. For these battles the *Sturmgewehr* would have been adequate. Maybe the tales were embroidered a bit to help the cause.

The Rheinmetall weapon was adopted by the Luftwaffe and known as the *Fallschirmjager Gewehr* 1942, or Parachutist's Rifle Model 1942. It was always abbreviated to FG 42. Although formally taken into service in 1942, it was still being modified and developed when the war ended, and so was never a completely finished design. It is now not known exactly how many of these weapons was made, and the Rheinmetall records have been lost, but a figure of 7,000 is frequently quoted, and there is little evidence to show that it was very much greater. This is a tiny and almost insignificant quantity in the production of a country at war, but events worked against the FG 42, and its sponsors were almost out of their proper line of business by the time it appeared as a complete weapon. While Crete reinforced the need for the FG 42 it also emphasized that similar large airborne assaults were too expensive in losses for the Germans to consider, and the parachutists became conventional ground forces with no more than a minor airborne role. This took a lot of the steam out of their argument for increased individual firepower, since there was plenty of conventional supporting fire to be had in the normal ground battle, artillery could be called up to support an assault, and machine guns were available to shoot in the leading troops. Factory capacity was scarce, and getting scarcer, and the ordnance office now had almost complete control over which weapons should be made. There is some doubt now as to when the FG 42 was first used in action, but if one German report is to be believed, it was the daring airborne raid which freed Mussolini in September 1943. Since there

was not much opposition this can hardly count as a decisive argument for FG 42, but it was also used in the Battle for Cassino, presumably in the hands of the 1st Parachute Division. Here again, it does not seem to have earned itself any particular mention, but then it was not ideally suited to that confused and bloody fight.

The area where it saw most action was in Western Germany itself during the last stages of the war, when it was issued to infantry units to replace other rifles lost in combat, or to equip fresh units for whom none other could be found. It was thus met quite frequently by US and British troops, and captured often. This fact may have led to the current belief that it existed in larger numbers than it actually did. As we have seen, it was a comparatively rare piece of equipment, even in the parachute forces, and it made little impression on tactics or design philosophy. For all this it was a good rifle,

**The German 7.92mm MP 44 Assault Rifle, developed despite Hitler's opposition**

the product of a very highly skilled design and development team. Providence should have been kinder to it.

As a weapon, the FG 42 is almost unique in the small arms world, and it is a complete contrast to all the other rifles produced during its lifetime. The general difficulty of producing an assault rifle firing full power ammunition has already been discussed and explained, and having stated that it is almost impossible to achieve, the FG 42 comes very close to being the exception which proves the rule. Although there are no revolutionary design features in it, it combines a variety of sound principles to produce what was a very competent selective fire weapon. The general shape is advanced for its time, the whole gun being in one straight line. The butt stock is small and squat, wasting little of the overall length. Early models had laminated wooden furniture, but some of the last had plastic. The pistol grip slopes back in a purposeful manner, though the angle is perhaps too acute for comfort in some firing positions. The receiver is made of steel stampings, but there is in fact a good deal of machining in the overall construction. The forestock is a wrap-around shape, made to fit the hand, and clamped to the barrel and gas cylinder. The barrel is quite long, but because it fits well back into the receiver the overall length of the gun is reasonably short. The forward hand grip is thick and robust, because the barrel and cylinder get hot quite quickly when firing automatic. A light metal bipod folds under the barrel, although tests in USA after the war concluded that it was not tough enough for normal use, and it had an irritating way of folding up while the gun was firing. A neat spike bayonet fitted into a lug at the muzzle, and when it was not in use it was turned round and travelled on its own lug with the point resting harmlessly against the forward hand grip, inside the bipod legs. The only possible objection to this very practical solution is that the soldier is always forced to carry his

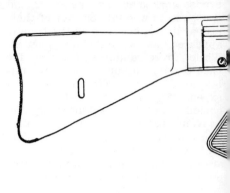

bayonet on the end of his rifle, whether he is using it or not, but the FG 42 bayonet was small and light, and made little difference to the balance or handling of the weapon.

The magazine held thirty rounds and fed in horizontally from the left. This is most unusual for a weapon of this calibre, and it tends to unbalance the gun when the magazine is full. The reason for doing this is not known now, but it may have been a desire to ensure that the firer could get low to the ground and still change magazines without difficulty. In contemporary publications of that time, some doubt was expressed on this subject, and Rheinmetall may have taken note of it. Also, it may have been an attempt to relieve the load on the magazine spring, which had to push thirty rounds into the feed way, and this would call for a strong spring if the lift was upwards and the gun vibrating. Whatever the reason, it was not successful and no other design copied it. In all other respects the FG 42 was sound and sensible. The mechanism was operated by gas, and it incorporated an entirely novel arrangement in the trigger release. When firing single shots the bolt closed onto the breech after each shot, having loaded another round. Each pull of the trigger simply released the firing pin, and so there was

The MP 43, MP 43/1, MP 44 and StG 44 Assault Rifles; *Calibre:* 7.92 Kurzi(PP 43 me); *System of Operation:* Gas. Selective fire; *Length:* 37 inches; *Barrel Length:* 16.5 inches; *Feed Device:* Detachable 30 Round, staggered row, box magaizne; *Sights: Front:* Hooded Barleycorn; *Rear:* Tangent with U notch; *Muzzle Velocity:* 2,132 feet per second; *Cyclic Rate:* 500 rpm

practically no movement of the weapon, nor any waste of time while the mechanism worked. In the technical expression of gun designers, the lock time was short. When the selection lever is turned to automatic fire a different series of events occurs. The bolt now stays to the rear after each burst, leaving the breech open and the feed way clear. The breech can now cool down to best advantage, and air can now round the heated bolt face and up the barrel. This also ensures that the next round to be fired will not 'cook off' from being kept in the hot breech. It is a most ingenious arrangement, and quite successful. The drawback is that it was more complicated to make and maintain than other trigger systems, and obviously cost more.

In fact, FG 42 was too expensive altogether, and it would have taken too much factory effort for it to be manufactured on a large scale. If the Luftwaffe had thought of asking for it in 1936 when they started to train a parachute force, the story might be very different, but by the end of 1942 the pressure was on Albert Speer and his production programme and there was no room for small numbers of time-consuming designs to be turned out.

FG has become a blind alley in the development of the assault rifle; it is not easy to shoot it accurately, despite its clever design, as the recoil is too great for comfort or consistent shooting. It weighs 9½lbs empty, an astonishingly low weight, but is very difficult to hold onto the target when firing automatic. Together with many other projects, it had to make way for the mass production of simpler and cheaper weapons, and its story really ended there.

The MP 43, 44, and FG 42 represent the whole field of assault rifles produced in the Second World War, and as with so many weapon developments in this century, the story is entirely German. Only Soviet Russia immediately followed the German lead, and they did this by first of all copying the ammunition. As early as 1943 there was a Russian version of the Kurz short round, although it was four years before they had a rifle in production which used it. This was the well known Kalashnikov AK 47 and its enormous success is really a distant and belated tribute to the small German team who laid down their ideas in 1938. A successor to the German MP44 assault rifle was built in Spain after 1945 and is known as the CETME. That design, somewhat modified, has now gone back to the West German army as their NATO rifle and so the wheel has turned full circle. Perhaps we have not made all that much progress after all.

# Machine guns

Second only to pistols in popular fascination are machine guns, and the list of them is almost endless. The modern machine gun came of age in the First World War, and rapidly dominated the static trench warfare, but in the Second World War it never managed to achieve the same importance. However, there were more of them, many more of them, and whenever the battle became static the machine gun ruled the infantry pattern of movement in much the same way as it had done twenty odd years before.

There were too many different guns in the Second World War to be able to do anything better in one chapter than skim over the field. By and large all the combatant armies started the war with too few modern machine guns for their armies, and in the rush to re-arm the factories could not keep pace. In every country, therefore, old stocks of obsolete guns were turned out and given to the troops, and quite often a variety of calibres was in service at the same time. In the German army particularly, when the *blitzkrieg* failed and the Eastern Front swallowed ever larger numbers of men and masses of material, second line troops and reservists carried a remarkable collection of weaponry, most of it commandeered from the occupied countries.

The British army seems to have been far more enterprising than most in its prewar machine gun procurement, for not only did it enter the war with good designs, but they were few, simple, reliable, and already produced

The Czechoslovakian ZB 26 light machine gun was the ancestor of the highly successful BREN

*eft:* Yugoslav partisans use the B30, a later model of the ZB26. Among other nations the Chinese adopted the ZB26 light machine gun to equip their forces

in quantity by the time the fighting started. Only the Vickers was a native design. This was really quite remarkble because there is always enormous reluctance to take on a foreign design unless it can possibly be helped. At east this is true in peace-time, in war anything goes. The First World War anded with the old Lewis as the standard light gun, and it was anything ut light. It also had an unenviable reputation for the ingenuity and number of its stoppages in acton, and by 931 it was well on its way out, to be replaced by the Vickers-Berthier. thers must write up the story of this an because it merits a little study, but never appeared in any except small numbers, in India. It was dropped in favour of a version of the Czech ZB 26,

known as the ZB 30. This was considered to be so far in advance of the VB that the latter was completely ousted.

The Czech company was asked to make new barrels to fit the .303 rimmed round, and also magazines. There were a few other changes as well, the barrel was shortened, the gas port moved back a bit, and the magazine enlarged to carry thirty rounds. By 1934 the new style gun was ready for testing again, and it was adopted in May 1935 as a replacement for the Lewis. It was just in time. Manufacturing rights were bought from Czechoslovakia and manufacture started in September 1937 at a pretty slow rate. The gun had now been given its name of Bren, derived from the initial letters of Brno the town and firm where it originated, and en from Enfield, the Royal Small Arms Factory where it was to be made. Six months later only 200 guns were complete, but production rose to 300 a week by the middle of 1938, and by the summer of 1940 over 30,000 had been made

117

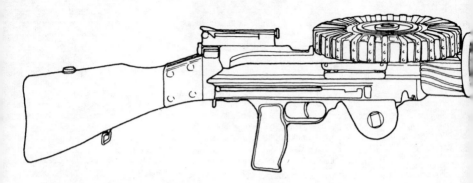

Mark 1 Lewis Machine Gun; *Calibre:* .303; *System of Operation:* Gas. Automatic fire only; *Weight:* 27 lbs; *Length:* 50.5 inches; *Feed Device:* 47 Round drum magazine. 97 Round drum magazine for aircraft use; *Sights: Front:* Barleycorn; *Rear:* Leaf with aperture; *Muzzle Velocity:* 2,440 feet per second.

*Below:* Developed by Colonel I N Lewis US but invented by Samuel McLean US the Lewis gun proved to be the mainstay of many services throughout the world

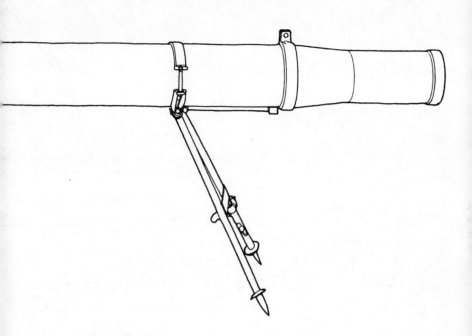

nd issued. Most of these were lost at Dunkirk, and about 2,500 survived in Britain to face the invasion.

The Lewis stepped back into the picture at this point, and 50,000 had to be taken out of store and refurbished. Most of these were aircraft guns left over from the First World War, and in addition to infantry units, they found their way onto merchant ships as an anti-aircraft gun of some limited value against the German dive bomber attacks in the coastal waters. But the Lewis also equipped all sorts of other little AA mountings around the country, most of them none too well sited.

Meanwhile frantic efforts at Enfield built up the stocks of Brens again, and the guns poured out for the remainder of the war, reaching about 1,000 a week by 1943 onwards. After 1945 no more were made, although many were refurbished and rebarrelled, and large stocks still remain in different parts of the world. There is no doubt that it is an extremely good gun, ideal as a light machine gun, its only fault being the

ammunition that it had to fire. Rebarrelled to 7.62mm NATO, it is still in service in the British army. It was probably the best ever light machine gun produced anywhere in the world to fire the old style full bore ammunition. Nowadays, with the smaller calibres and higher performances from bullets, it may no longer hold its own so well, but let us be in no doubt that in its day it was, despite its few faults, a supreme weapon. We have said in the chapter on rifles that there is no quicker way of being thrown out of a British Army Veterans meeting than to suggest that the Lee Enfield could not shoot straight. Try suggesting that the Bren was not a good gun and you risk having your teeth rammed down your throat as well. There is still a strong section of the present British army that contends that the Bren has not yet been superseded, and it remains standard issue for jungle and Far Eastern stations. It fought throughout the war in all theatres and continents, and the factories managed

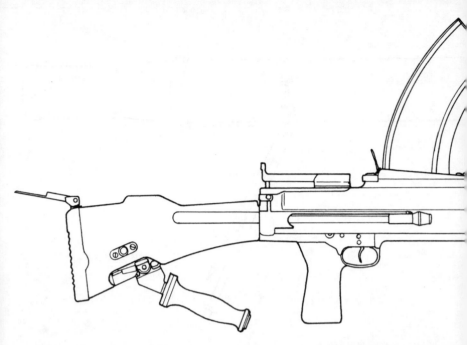

Bren LMG Mk I; *Calibre:* .303; *System of Operation:* Gas, Selective fire; *Length:* 45.5 inches; *Barrel Length:* 25 inches; *Feed Device:* 30 Round box or 100 Round drum; *Front Sights:* Blade with ears; *Rear Sights:* Aperture with radial drum *Weight:* 22.12 lbs; *Muzzle Velocity:* 2,440 feet per second; *Cyclic Rate:* 500 rpm

A British Bren gunner in action in Normandy, 1944

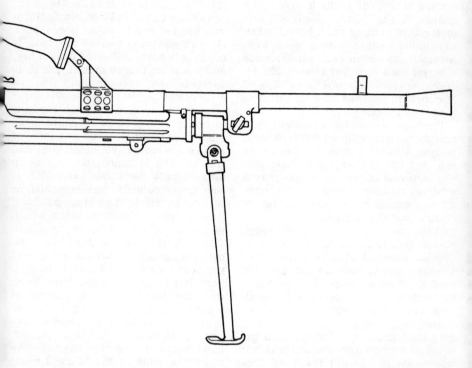

to keep up the flow of replacements (just), so that although stocks were critical just after Dunkirk, they never reached the same low level again.

It is worth describing the Bren in some detail because the design recurs so often that it will then be only necessary to refer back to the one weapon rather than endlessly repeat the same data. It is a gas operated gun, magazine fed, of conventional and simple design, rugged, fairly light and possessing few vices. One can congratulate the Czech firm on having done a good job. The gas cylinder is underneath the barrel, and just over half the length on the .303 version. In this it differed from the original because the gas cylinder there was as long as the barrel and ran to the muzzle. At the gas port

is an easily adjustable plug which gives four different settings, so enabling the gunner to take up any variation in the rate of fire, or compensate for fouling or dirt in the mechanism. This ability to vary the power of a gun is a valuable adjunct, and one which is not always found on the so-called advanced guns of today. All the Bren gunner had to do was to poke the nose of a round into a slot in the gas plug and rotate it to the next bigger hole, a matter of ninety degrees, and done within a few seconds. The barrel was a quick change type, held by a sliding plug at the gas port (which came off with it), and a coarse threaded nut at the breech. A quarter turn with a handle attached to the nut releases the barrel, which is then lifted off by the carrying handle, and replaced by another. It takes about six or seven seconds, and there are few guns which can equal it. It is worth digressing for a moment to say that even now, in 1971, there are three machine guns in service in various armies in the world which have quick change barrels but absolutely no method of holding that barrel when the gunner wants to take it off the gun. After firing a couple of hundred rounds a barrel gets very hot indeed, 500 degrees centigrade is not unusual, and human skin makes a poor insulator at those temperatures.

The receiver and gas cylinder are in one piece, and machined from the same forging, with magazine housing on the top, and the trigger mechanism pinned on to the underside. At the rear is a fairly substantial buffer which takes up any excess energy left in the recoiling parts. The magazine is curved to take the .303 round, and although scaled to take thirty, it was more normally loaded with twenty-nine or twenty-eight to ease the difficulties of feeding which accompanied the .303 in any machine gun. Rimless ammunition gives a straight magazine and fewer stoppages. In some ways it is a pity that the gun did not retain the original 7.92mm ammunition which it was made for, as did the Besa. The magazine opening has a sliding cover to close it and keep out dirt, as does the ejection port under the receiver: the latter usually the subject of vulgar jokes when recruits have difficulty in operating the awkward catch which holds it open.

A bipod pivots on the gas cylinder at the forward end, with adjustable legs. The furniture is wood, and the sights were first of all a drum and arm backsight, but later a simple sliding leaf. The foresight is on the barrel, thereby allowing each barrel to be matched to the gun, because all zeroing is done by moving the foresight. All-up weight was 22lbs with the .303 version, and it shot well out to 600 yards or more. A change lever allowed single shots to be fired, and gunners were always trained to use these whenever possible. There were some accessories, or optional extras as we would say now, which came with the gun. One was the tripod, a strangely continental idea which ruined any pretensions to a light machine gun. It weighed another 20lbs or so and only offered a stable platform in a limited arc. In other words, once the gun was pinned onto the tripod, it could only cover a limited field of fire, and it was no longer mobile, which is surely the major requirement of such a class of gun. Anyway, the tripod never saw much service in real earnest, although it was made in quite large quantities, and it was a waste of money. It could be stood on end like the MG 34 tripod and used as an anti-aircraft mounting, at which it was conspicuously unsuccessful; or it could permit shooting on fixed lines or pre-registered points, which is rarely called for from an LMG. The soldiers cursed it. One other curiosity of the Mark 1 Bren was a second pistol grip below the butt for the gunner's left hand, and a top strap to go over the shoulder. Neither survived long, the lower pistol grip being the first to go as British gunners have never held guns in that way, the left hand always going over the top. The top strap went in the Mark 2 when production was simplified.

There are few real weaknesses to the basic Bren, the magazine being the single most troublesome feature. As with any rimmed cartridge, unless the rounds are fed in rim in front of rim the feed will jam, and this was the most frequent cause of stoppages on the war-time models. Despite the relatively simple design, there were many machining operations in the manufacture, particularly of the receiver, but this was endemic to guns of that period, and while it was a drawback, it was not one that worried the soldier. The Bren was backed up by a far more venerable piece of minor ordnance, the Vickers Medium Machine Gun, which was held at Battalion. By 1939 the Vickers was already nearly fifty-seven

*Above:* A member of the Netherlands Brigade mans a Bren. *Below:* Fifth Army Vickers machine gunners at Cassino

years old, although that is really computed from the date of its predecessor, the Maxim. But the difference was slight, and barely worth worrying about. The Vickers itself was introduced into service in 1912, and was about one-third lighter than the Maxim, turning the scales at 40lbs, plus a little bit. The tripod weighed another 40lbs or more, and so the total load was considerable, requiring three men in a team to carry it in its component parts. It was never a truly man-portable weapon, and indeed was never meant to be, although there are hundreds of men alive today who have sweated and humped it over all sorts of country in all parts of the world. It was originally intended in its Maxim form to be wheeled about on a small carriage, and it was so in its early days, but the Vickers grew away from this idea, and had to be carried. In Burma it was on mules, in the desert on jeeps, in Italy and France on carriers, and everywhere on men's backs. It was awkward, heavy, cumbersome, and well loved because it did what was required of it – it gave covering fire. Reliability was its outstanding virtue, and there are plenty of well authenticated stories of the fabulous amounts of ammunition fired by Vickers guns virtually without stopping.

The best example of continuous fire really belongs to the First World War, but it is worth retelling out of context because it applies equally well to the Second World War, and was undoubtedly very nearly, if not actually repeated in the classic formal battles such as Alamein and the Mareth Line. On the Somme in 1916 was the 100th company of the Machine Gun Corps (a special corps formed in the First World War to use machine guns in the support role). On the 24th August it had ten Vickers guns in position and was ordered to support an attack with rapid fire. An area had to be neutralized for twelve hours to prevent any enemy crossing it during that period. The range was 2,000 yards. Some infantry were provided to act as ammunition carriers and water parties. The guns fired at the rapid rate for the required twelve hours with no major break downs, and all were in action at the end of the time. Each gun had fired an average of 8,300 rounds, making a grand total for the 10 of 1,000,000. The best gun fired at the rate of 10,000 rounds per hour, the others slightly less. Each gun would have had to change its barrel at about 10,000 rounds so that 100 or so barrels must have been used. Water for cooling the barrels was required in continuous quantities, and only just lasted the action. A hand driven machine for filling belts was worked throughout, but can hardly have kept pace, so that considerable stocks of filled belts must have been dumped beforehand. Later it was found that the target area had been kept completely clear of all movement during the twelve hours. One can hardly be surprised at that! 1,000,000 rounds is an awful lot to have falling on one piece of countryside, and quite apart from the lethality of them, the noise of their arrival must have sounded like a non stop Western film.

The action on the Somme was the most intense and the longest recorded for Vickers, but it is a wonderful example of what the gun could do, and the Second World War version differed in no way worth mentioning from the one of twenty-five years before. It was a water cooled, belt fed, recoil operated gun of fairly massive construction, and complicated design. Manufacture was on traditional lines, involving machining of many parts and the use of metals that were hard to get in war time. The barrel was cooled by $7\frac{1}{2}$ pints of water, which was not easy to find in some parts of the world, which quickly evaporated to steam after prolonged firings, and has been known to give away the position of the gun by the tell-tale plume of white rising from the condensor can. Stoppages were frequent, and causes for them totalled about twenty-five in all. An unprotected crank handle flew back and forth on the right hand side while the gun

fired, and the gunner who was holding the firing grips soon suffered from a form of mechanical Saint Vitus' dance. But it worked, and was hardly ever known not to work. In fact it became a by-word for reliability. It was officially and prematurely retired from service in the British army in 1961 amid scenes of ceremony and grief. The last guns were still in service in 1965, but went soon after that, mourned by all. This extraordinary affection was engendered by one virtue only, that of reliability, and it shows how much it is valued by the soldier. But naturally the Vickers was not the only gun to perform so well, its reputation is shared by all the Maxim derivations.

The combination of Bren and Vickers served well, and no changes were made throughout the war. The one complemented the other ideally; the Bren giving mobile fire support to the squad, and the Vickers the longer range and more deliberately planned support both in defence and attack.

**The Carrier Bren No 2 Mark I gave protection and manoeuvrability to the light machine gun**

The Bren was sometimes moved about the battlefield on the Universal carrier, or Bren Gun Carrier as it was originally known, and in the later years of the war the Vickers was put on to the same vehicle when it had been found to be unsuited to carrying Brens. In fact the so-called Bren carrier became the infantry's maid of all work, being used for all support weapons, but its story belongs to another place, and it can only be mentioned here in respect of its original role. The intention was to give the Bren protection and mobility on the battlefield, but the trenches of Flanders did not reappear in 1940, and it is no good moving the squad machine gun if the squad cannot move in the same way also. It could not, because the days of the armoured infantry had still to come, and so the

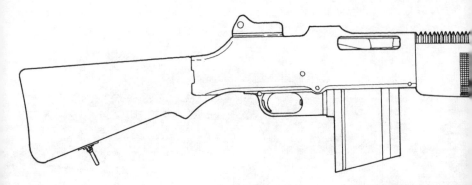

Browning Automatic Rifle Model 1922; *Calibre:* .30; *System of Operation:* Gas.
Selective fire; *Length:* 41 inches; *Barrel Length:* 18 inches; *Feed Device:*
Staggered row, detachable box magazine, 20 Round capacity; *Sights: Front:*
Hooded Blade; *Rear:* Leaf W/Aperture, adjustable for windage; *Weight:* 19.2 lbs;
*Muzzle Velocity:* Approx 2,700 feet per second; *Cyclic Rate:* 550 rpm

vehicle passed to other users.

But so much for the fairly simple British picture. Turning now to the USA, the story becomes more interesting. The policy at the beginning of the war was quite clear. The squad had the Browning Automatic Rifle, and company and battalion support was given by the Browning Model 1919 This idea was very similar to the British one, although the light machine guns differ considerably. Critics of the BAR have to tread warily, because this gun arouses the same feelings of loyalty in ex-GIs as does the Bren in Britain. However, these same GIs can usually be persuaded to admit that the Bren was the better of the two, without prejudicing the BAR. But a study of the BAR does show that it lacked many of the qualities needed to make it a really worthwhile squad gun, and the design seems to fall midway between that of an automatic rifle and a machine gun with most of the vices of both. It had been designed in 1916 by John Brown-

ing to be a light shoulder fired rifle to be used in the advance across No Man's Land, and fired while on the move. It never succeeded in being a light rifle, and weighed 16 lbs from the start. When firing automatic the vibration was too great to hold the gun onto the target, and the bipod issued with the Second World War models was heavy and clumsy. It was difficult to adjust, and most gunners ended up by throwing it away and reverting to using the weapon as a rifle. The barrel could not be changed, and so there was no capability for any form of sustained fire, and the magazine held only twenty rounds. Really the kindest thing that one can say about the BAR is that it was a compromise which did not work out.

It was gas operated, with an action that involved a rather complicated stripping procedure, later to be modified by FN of Belgium in the post-war models. For all its faults, and the foregoing catalogue is probably more than enough to get the author tarred

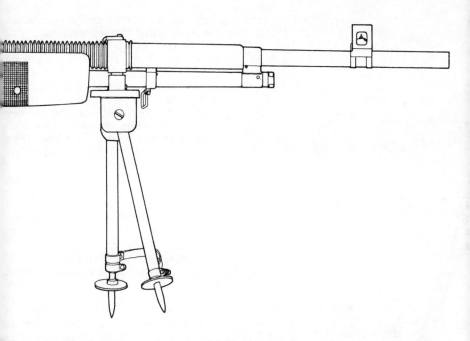

The rapid firing Browning automatic rifle model 1942

and feathered by Second World War veterans, the Browning Automatic Rifle was used in several countries in the 20s and 30s, and was even issued to the British Home Guard in sizeable quantities in the hazy and dangerous days of 1940 and '41. It stayed in US service until the Korean War, and for a few years afterwards, probably spanning forty years of continuous use before it was finally replaced by that phenomenon of the middle 20th Century, a general purpose machine gun. It still soldiers on in a variety of Asian countries. How many were made is not at all clear, but it must have been upwards of a couple of million in the whole time of its service, and a large proportion have survived.

Looking at the infantry weapon armoury of the US Army as it entered the Second World War, one cannot help but notice the lack of an effective squad light machine gun, and it is a thousand pities that General MacArthur was not able to get one. One wonders if he ever tried, but even if he had, the financial climate of his day would undoubtedly have killed it, and he might have lost the Garand also. But what a wonderful combination the squad could have had with the Garand and a .30 Bren!

In fact a light machine gun did figure in the American squad but only in Marine and certain special units; this was the Johnson, a light machine gun developed by the same company in the same time scale as the Johnson rifle whose story has already been told. The light machine gun was a straight derivative of the rifle, and employed the same method of operation, namely short recoil. Many of the parts were interchangeable, and like the rifle it had several unusual features. It was designed to fire semi automatically from the closed bolt for accuracy, and on full automatic the bolt remained open between shots

**US troops armed with the Browning automatic rifle on Okinawa**

o prevent a chambered round from verheating and 'cooking off'. The nagazine only held twenty rounds rhich was a drawback, and was unsual in feeding into the left side of he receiver. Like the rifle, the feed .ps were in the receiver, and, also .ke the rifle, the magazine could e topped up with single rounds :d in from the right hand side. nfortunately, all that weight on ne side of the gun unbalanced , and tended to make it difficult ) fire at times. But the overall eight was low at just over 14lbs, nd the Marines considered it to e an automatic rifle, which it efinitely was not. Like the rifle, it )ok apart into small packages, and ) found some favour with paratroops, .t orders were small, and only 10,000 ere manufactured in the whole time ∴ its existence. Despite an improved ·44 model which overcame the objec-ons to the earlier models in that ey could not work in adverse contions, the Johnson was dropped, and `ter 1944 none was made. It was a range design, a blind alley on the ·th towards small arms perfection, .t it had many good features, though it was never a genuine light achine gun in the generally accep-d sense of the term. It was too light id the mechanism was insufficiently werful to ensure continuous action der bad conditions. Mud and dirt .ickly defeated it.

Supporting machine gun fire was ven by the Browning medium gun, veteran of the First World War, and .twardly remarkably like the British ckers. The US Army started the cond World War with both a water oled and an air cooled version of the owning, both of them being the same n except for the barrel. The basic n was robust and recoil operated, eding from a cloth belt or a dis-tegrating link belt. It was immense-strong and reliable, and involved ιaller accelerating masses than the ckers so that its rate of fire was pable of adaptation up to at least

1,000 rounds a minute, and a version was used in large numbers for aircraft which fired at this rate. The water cooled gun and its tripod mount weighed almost the same as the Vickers at about 80lbs, and had an almost identical performance. Indeed, at first glance it is easy to mistake one for the other, though the first immediate identifying feature of the Browning is the pistol grip at the rear of the receiver. The jacket held seven pints of water just as did the Vickers, but it had a rather neat trombone type arrangement of pipes which sent steam along various ways to the condenser can. No doubt this was worthwhile, but it looks now to have been a complication that could have been avoided, and so have led to slightly simpler manufacture. This gun was steadily replaced by the air cooled version as the war went on, and it ended its fighting days in the weapons company of the battalion, while the air cooled one was much more widespread.

The air cooled gun dated back to 1918, and was no more than the M 1917A1 water cooled gun with a heavy barrel on it, and a small perforated steel jacket round it. It weighed 44lbs, including its mount, but otherwise performed in exactly the same way as the heavier gun, even to being able to keep up very nearly the same rate of sustained fire. This was good, but not good enough, and throughout the war the US Ordnance Department attempted to produce a light machine gun, but it was by then too late. As the Infantry Board said in 1942, ' . . . based on past experience the Board believes that the time consumed in the development, technical testing, adoption as standard for issue, set up for manufacture, and distribution to the services, will be so great that under the best conditions of acceler-ated procedure, it will be a distant date in the future when the weapon can be placed in the hands of the troops.' How right they were! And how neatly they worded it. Attempts

*Above:* The .30 Johnson model 1941 light machine gun was used in limited numbers in the South-East Asian campaign. *Below:* The .50 Browning heavy barrel M2 machine gun jeep mounted ready for action

*Above:* A later development of the First World War, the air-cooled .30 M 1919 machine gun saw wide service during the Second World War. *Below:* The .30 Browning M 1917 water-cooled machine gun on a M 1917 A1 tripod

were then made to make a light machine gun from the air cooled M 1917A4 gun by stripping off as much as possible, putting on a light barrel, a shoulder stock, and a small bipod, which the Infantry Board piously hoped would result in a satisfactory LMG. It did not, of course, it produced rather a horrid bastard which weighed over 32lbs and lacked power in the mechanism. It was adopted on 17th February, 1943, and after further modifications a small number was issued to field units. One hopes they were grateful. These unsatisfactory compromises show that the lack of an LMG was felt keenly in some quarters, and make it even more a matter for regret that none was produced before the war started. But this does not detract from the story of the Browning, and this was truly one of the great weapons of the war. There must be records somewhere of how many have been made, but they are not available at the moment. The gun has been produced in forty or more different models and calibres and used in eleven major countries in the world as well as innumerable smaller ones. It was a highly successful aircraft gun, and still is so used, despite the design being fifty-five years old, and it is not too wild a guess to say that twenty years from now Brownings will still be tapping away in some part of the world, and the finger on the trigger will be brown, or black, or yellow, or white, or any other you like, and the bullets may be travelling eastwards or westwards, it makes no difference.

In Germany the machine gun story is very like the rifle story. There was a clearly laid down policy, and approved types were accepted for service. As with the rifles, production could not keep pace with the demands, and anyway these had started a bit too late to allow supplies to be ready in quantity for the war, and so one can find dozens of machine gun types in service in one or other unit of the army. However, front line infantry units all kept to the same gun, and this was the Maschinengewehr 1934 or MG 34. Later it was replaced, or rather reinforced, by the MG 42, but more of that later. We must first go back to the reasoning and thought behind the MG 34 because this coloured all subsequent design of machine guns in Nazi Germany.

After the First World War the restrictions of the Versailles Treaty meant that very little actual weapon development could be undertaken in Germany itself. The enormous factory which had turned out the thousands of Maxims was dismantled, and the small German army was limited to specific numbers of weapons. In a way this was just as much a help as the Allied bombing of the Second World War has now proved to be for with no stocks of old weapons to use up, and few inhibitions in tactical thinking, there was a certain amount of experiment and enlargement of the lessons learned in Flanders.

Although little attention was paid to rifles, machine guns benefited to a greater extent than elsewhere, and the result was that when Hitler came to power there was a complete design waiting to be made, and some quite good ideas on how to employ it. The gun derived from a Swiss model of 1930, the Solothurn MG 30, and it is no accident that the factory was controlled financially by Germany. This particular gun was almost a straight line layout, and outwardly appears to be very simple. It is not quite so straightforward when looked at from the inside, but it is remarkably compact. The operating system is short recoil, and, as the barrel and bolt move back, the bolt is unlocked by two rollers which move in cams in the receiver, they cause the bolt to rotate and move its locking lugs out of engagement with the barrel. The barrel then gives the bolt a final flip backwards, and returns itself to battery. The bolt runs freely back until the spring pushes it forward again, and chambers the next round, rotating itself into lock as it does so. The

*ove and below:* The German 7.92mm MG34 machine gun was one of the war's
ost extensively used guns. Adaptable to bi-pod, tripod or AA mounting, it served
th the Wehrmacht and Luftwaffe throughout the conflict

*Above:* A German soldier takes aim with his MG 34. *Below:* Twin MG 34s on anti-aircraft mountings. These weapons were adapted according to circumstanc

stem is notable for the low weight
the moving masses once unlocked
om the barrel, and it allows a high
te of fire with little modification.
he initial movement of combined
rrel and bolt provides a large
ough mass to absorb the recoil and
ansfer it to the gun over a period of
ne which is sufficient to allow it to
controlled better by the gunner
an if the system had been, for
stance, gas operated. Further con-
ol is provided by the fact that the
signer laid out the barrel, receiver
d butt all in one straight line, and
transferred the push to the gunner's
oulder without too much upward
ovement. Finally, on all the guns
ich followed this design, the bipod
s put well up the barrel, almost
the muzzle, and this is usually
koned to help stability.

his sounds to have been a paragon
a gun, but it cannot have been all
t good, and was turned down by the
hrmacht. However, it was im-
ved, and accepted in 1934, where-
n Mauser did some more work on it
enable production to start in 1936.
e gun that they made was the MG 34,
l it was beautifully machined and
shed, almost too beautifully fin-
ed in fact. It took a lot of making,
l by the height of the war there
e four factories in Germany mak-
MG 34, and one in occupied Czecho-
vakia, and still there were not
ugh.

he MG 34 fired a belt of ammuni-
n, with fifty rounds to a belt, and
barrel could be changed fairly
ckly, though not all that easily,
a typically German kit of spares
extras came with each gun. It had
ripod, and this could be modified
stood on end to make an anti-
raft mounting. The rate of fire was
sually high at 800-900 a minute.
er models went a bit higher than
to near 1,000 a minute. Finally,
trigger did not pull in the usual
, but rocked about a central pin.
ling the upper half gave single
ts, and the lower half fired auto-

matic. This was directly lifted from
the Solothurn gun, and it was not sub-
sequently used on other designs.

The notable thing about the MG 34
was that it was another 'first'. It was,
in fact, the first general purpose
machine gun, a type that has now become almost universal, and its genesis
sprang from the German philosophy
regarding the use of machine guns
based on their experiences in the trench
warfare of 1918. In that war the machine
gun was king. Infantry could never
move against dug-in machine guns
unless they were inside armoured
vehicles, so the Germans came to look
on the main infantry weapon as being
the squad machine gun. The purpose of
the riflemen was to back up the gun, but
all the work was done by the gun, or so
they reasoned. Britain and the US
thought differently, and stuck to the
rifle as the predominant infantry arm.
In Britain the gun provided fire power,
but the rifles backed it up and provided
the manoeuvre element, as well as
being considered to be at least the
equal of the gun in bullet production.
The US relied on the semi-automatic
Garand to provide almost all the
squad fire.

Thinking the way they did, the German army was prepared to put more
infantry effort into the squad gun than
were the Allies, and it was the focus of
the squad's tactics. The gun team was
always two men, and occasionally
three, and they usually appear in
photographs swathed in belts of ammunition which this fast firing gun
gobbled up as quickly as they could
feed them in. It was never a real light
machine gun in the generally accepted
sense of the word, it weighed just over
26lbs with bipod, and a 50-round belt
added a further 5lbs. A tripod and telescopic sight turned the gun into a
passable medium gun, and it was then
used to give support fire to the company and battalion. The quick change
barrel allowed it to fire for considerable periods of time, although to do so
required that several spare barrels
were available on the position. Thus

one gun did for all purposes, and it was also the standard tank gun. Most countries have now come to do the same thing and they look upon it as some new idea dreamed up after 1945.

The MG 34 had some faults, and among them was a reluctance to fire in adverse conditions such as mud, sand, and snow. This, coupled with its demands on factory effort, led to the introduction of the MG 42. Originally intended to replace the MG 34, the 42 was never made in sufficient quantities to do so, and until the end of the war 34s continued to be made and 42s supplemented them. If the war had gone as the Germans intended it, it would all have been over by 1941, and the MG 34 would have sufficed. As it turned out, an enormous army had to be mobilised to deal with a war on two fronts and the supply of machine guns quickly ran out. It was sheer luck that the MG 42 turned out to be as successful as it did. The general outline is, of course, very similar to the MG 34, and not easy to tell apart at some distance; but the locking system is different, the barrel change greatly improved, and the rate of fire increased to the remarkable figure of 1,200, and sometimes 1,300, rounds per minute. This gave it an immediately recognizable audible signature in which the explosions so run together that it almost sounds like tearing cloth. It is quite fearsome, and, no doubt, very encouraging for the man pulling the trigger, but it caused the gun to be highly innaccurate after the first few shots had left the barrel because the movement is so excessive. In fact, the whole thing all but walks away from the gunner. The Germans were well aware of this but felt that it was worth while. The design started in 1941, using some ideas which are reputed to have come from Poland. Much work was done to incorporate stampings in the manufacture, and only the bolt, barrel, and a few other parts had to be machined. Indeed, the most striking thing about the gun is its rough appearance and apparent lack of finesse,

but it performed incredibly well fro the very beginning, and is one of t success stories of the war. The fir ones went to North Africa in t spring of 1942, and production was full swing by the end of the year wh issues were being made througho the German army.

MG 42 only fired automatic, the being no way of selecting single sho The locking system performed well mud and sand, although stoppa still occurred from time to time, p sibly from the mechansim being ov strained by the high rate of fire. A f minor changes were brought in as p duction increased, but they only volved such items as cocking hand and the material of the stock. By a large the 1941 design remained changed until 1945. The gun was a popular with Allied troops, and c tured ones were often used in act against their late owners; in fact US Army did seriously consider us a version of the MG 42 as a possible placement for the BAR. There is a lo and rather dry account in the reco of the Aberdeen Proving Ground wh relates how an MG 42 was cop (modesty prevents the name of firm being quoted), and after m reworking of parts and rejection sub-contract items, the gun was re for test in February 1944. A long durance test was started, but pro to be so disastrously bad that it abandoned after less than 1,500 rou had been fired. An enormous wi hunt was held, and some time late was discovered that the receiver been made a quarter of an inch short, and but for that element mistake by some unknown draug man the US Army might, just mi have had a copy of the MG 42 by the of the war.

MG 42 continues in service in West German army under the nam G1 machine gun, but it is aln

**MG 42. Top: Bipod extended**
**Centre: Plan view**
**Lower: Carrying position**

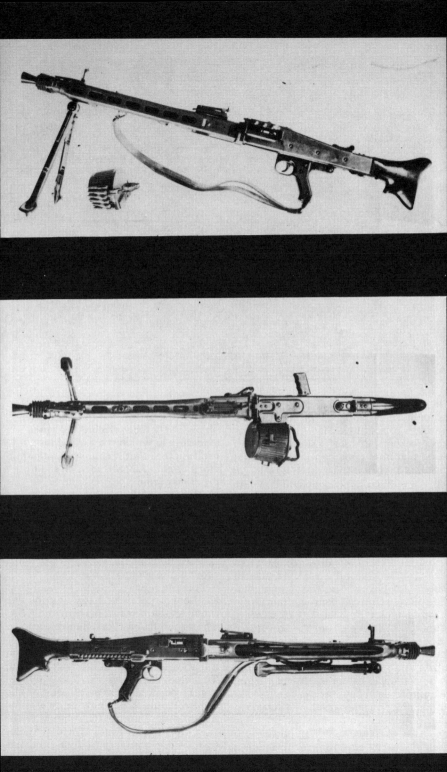

identical with the 1944 model, except that it is chambered for the NATO 7.62mm round. It is also in use in several other armies. Knowing how long machine guns can last, it would not be surprising to find it still in active service twenty or thirty years from now. These two, the MGs 34 and 42, constitute the only native designs of infantry machine gun used by the Germans. There were some other guns pressed into service, but they all started life with other intentions. When the shortage became really acute in the latter part of the war, some curious adaptations appeared. One was a ground mount for the MG 15 aircraft gun. MG 15 derived from the Solothurn Model 30, and so was a cousin of MG 34, but on the way it had become long and slim, and it only fired automatic, and only took a 75-round saddle magazine. An improvised butt stock was fitted, a bipod hung on the barrel, and standard sights pinned onto the barrel. The result is clumsy, heavy and much too long to carry in comfort. It made a poor infantry gun. Other guns used were those captured from France or Czechoslovakia, and the Czech version of the British Bren actually served in the German army though only with second line occupation forces.

Turning now to Russia, we find that the Soviet policy on machine guns was much the same as in Britain and USA. The squad had a light machine gun to back up the rifle fire, and support for the company and battalion came from a heavy and less mobile medium gun. The Red Army was extensively re-organised in the 1920s, and one of the requirements in the new army was for a light machine gun. They were aware that few of the First World War designs were worth pursuing, and set about developing a home produced model. The Degtyarev was adopted in 1927, the originator being V A Degtyarev, an employee of the Tula Arsenal. There were several remarkable things about the Degtyarev design that make it a landmark in the progress of the light machine gun, but the most intriguing thing is the fact that the entire operating system uses only six moving parts. As with so many other Soviet weapons, simplicity is the keynote throughout, and this time lightness is also important. The loaded gun weighs only 26lbs. It is a conventional gas operated weapon, easily distinguished by its flat pan magazine which sits on top of the receiver in the same way as the Lewis drum did. This drum is the weak spot of the gun because it is made of rather light gauge metal, and is easily damaged, but it is the best way of feeding the old fashioned rimmed 7.62mm 1908 pattern round which the Degtyarev had to fire.

Forty-seven rounds were loaded singly into the pan, to lie in one layer with their bullet points inwards to the centre. Three pans were carried in a tin box which protected them to some extent, though made a clumsy load to carry, and some were carried in canvas bags. The Degtyarev was tried out in the Spanish Civil War, and by 1939 was the major automatic weapon of the Russian army. A later variant of it is still in service in the USSR, although now the pan magazine has been replaced by a belt, and the calibre has changed to the intermediate round of the Kalashnikov.

The back-up or supporting machine gun for the company and battalion was either the venerable Maxim, or the later SGM Guryonov. The Maxim was no different from any other except that in its Russian version it achieved the all time record for weight, topping the scales at 52½lbs for the bare gun. Quite obviously such a

*Above:* The Degtyarev 7.62mm DP light machine gun, was, together with the PPSh, the best known weapon of the USSR during the war. *Below and right:* Red Army troops bring up their wheeled DS M 1939 heavy machine guns

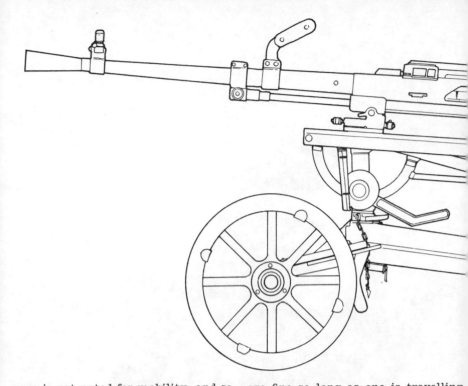

gun is not noted for mobility, and so started the curious and entirely Russian idea of putting little wheels onto the mount. Perhaps other countries did this in the early days of machine guns, indeed it was the fashion to put the first Maxims on a light field gun mount, with large wheels, horse teams and all; but it soon died out as it was realised that to employ such a gun properly it had to be up with the front line infantry, and no one wants a field gun sitting in his position. So the man-portable tripods and bipods appeared, and the last use of the field gun type of carriage was in the Boer War and the Boxer Rising. It would seem that this message never got through entirely to the Russians, who fitted their 1910 Maxim with small wheels and a trail. They then went further and added a bullet-proof shield, and the weight of the entire gun now reached the ridiculous figure of 152lbs, give or take a pound or two, and demanded a crew of three men as a minimum. These small wheeled carriages

are fine so long as one is travelling along hard roads or tracks, but come to mud or ditches or sand, and the gun crew then has to carry the gun and carriage. Even the Russian peasant must have found 152lbs a tall order to hump about. The shield was discreetly dropped after the first six months or so of the war with Germany, though it appeared often enough in the Finnish war. In winter the gun had a little sledge, which may have been quite practical. Certainly, it would not suffer from the same drawbacks as the wheels. There are still some newsreel pictures of the first winter of the German war showing white clad gun teams running across snow hauling their Maxims on sledges, and a few even still have the shield fitted. But the wheels died hard, and when the Maxim was replaced by the Guryonov that too had a carriage. In many parts of the world it still has, because it is still in service in many communist countries and the Chinese particularly went in for slavish copies of the Soviet origi-

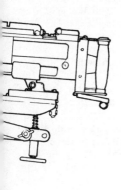

**Goryunov Heavy Machine Gun M 1943 (SG43)**; *Calibre:* 7.62mm; *System of Operation:* Gas. Automatic; *Length:* 44.09 inches; *Barrel Length:* 28.3 inches; *Feed Device* 250 Round Metallic Link Belt; *Sights: Front:* Blade. *Rear:* Leaf; *Weight: Gun:* 29.76 lbs; *Mount:* 50.9 lbs; *Muzzle Velocity:* 2,870 feet per second; *Cyclic Rate:* 600-700 rpm

The Goyronov held its own against German weapons

nals. At least the Guryonov did not fit the shield, but without it it weighed 90lbs, ready to move, without ammunition. God help the Russian machine gunner!

Neither of these support machine guns was remarkable in any particular way. The Guryonov was introduced in 1943 to replace the Maxim, but it never did so entirely because of production difficulties, and the Maxim was still in front line service in 1945. The Guryonov was an air cooled gun, 20lbs lighter than the Maxim, and with a quick change barrel of generous dimensions. One might even describe the barrel as large, because it is a prominent feature of the gun, and would stand up to 500 rounds of continuous fire before needing to be changed. It must have been a good design because it was retained in service when the Soviet army changed over to its present range of postwar small arms, and to keep the Guryonov meant keeping the old rimmed round as well. It was really a tank gun which strayed into the infantry field, and it is still fitted to some Soviet armoured vehicles; probably this vehicle ancestry gives it the heavy barrel, for tank gunners are renowned for blasting off whole belts of ammunition at one go. A final word on the Guryonov must be said about its anti-aircraft mount. There is a charming sketch in existence copied from a Soviet training pamphlet showing two impeccably dressed soldiers, looking as though butter wouldn't melt in their mouths, with the wheeled mount of their Guryonov standing on end on its wheels, and the gun pivoting on the point of the trail, pretending to lay an aim on an aeroplane. Maybe it works, maybe it does not, it looks a most uncomfortable operation and one would imagine that at certain positions of traverse the whole thing is going to fall over into the gunner's face. At least it gave the pilot a sporting chance.

The other Big League machine gun makers were Italy and Japan. Both offer a complicated and confusing picture, but we will look at the Italian scene first. It has already been told how the Italian army started the war in a rare state of confusion due to the fact that there had been a sudden shift in government financial policy which stopped a change in calibre just as it got nicely under away. The resulting chaos affected the machine guns of the army, just as much as it did the rifles. One unusual result was that at one time or another at least seven different calibres were in use in the various models of infantry guns, excluding the 20mm ex-aircraft guns. In the Italian army if nowhere else, supply officers worked for their living. The number of different guns in use is almost as long as the list of ammunition, so that it will need some simplification in order to follow easily. Starting with the light machine guns, the standard model was the Breda Model 30, which is worth describing in some detail because it is interesting in many respects.

It was in 6.5mm, and straight away strikes the eye because it is so ugly and ungainly looking. Angular bits stick out from it in all directions, and there are holes and slots everywhere. It does not compare with the elegance and line of the MG 34 and 42, or even a Bren. The barrel lies in a sort of trough, the magazine is a permanent fixture, sticking out to one side, and the butt stock and trigger group look as if they were clipped on afterwards to the back of the receiver. It must have been hell to clean, and sheer murder in the desert. The final blow to the wretched gunner is the fact that there is no actual carrying handle, so that the whole awkward outfit had to be cradled in the arms or held by the folding bipod and pistol grip, with all those bits and pieces catching in his clothing and equipment. The system of operation was novel for a light gun as it was a form of delayed blowback in which the barrel moved back as well as the bolt, hence the trough for the barrel, as it needed a bearing surface at the front. After a short travel,

A 6.5mm Breda model 30 machine gun in action against the French during the short campaign of 1940

lt and barrel parted, and the usual tions of ejection, feed, and chamber- were carried out. One immediate ag to moving the barrel is that the esight has to be on the body of the n, and so is not lined up with the rrel itself; so, if the barrel is anged, the new one may easily be t of line with the sights. Quite turally, this does not lead to at accuracy of shooting.

he blowback system suffered from ack of power in certain conditions, d would fail to extract a fired tridge. This was overcome by anging for an oil pump to squirt a y amount of oil into each cartridge it fed into the breech. This was no w idea, it had already appeared in er Italian designs, and one might ve expected that by 1930 its appal- g limitations would have been lised, but there were some countries ich were almost deliberately back- rd looking in their weapon design, d Italy was undoubtedly one of se during the 1930s. Any oiling

system is simply asking for trouble in dust or sand, and the Breda was no exception. The mechanism quickly became fouled up with a sticky mixture of grit and oil, and some burnt carbon from the breech.

The magazine of this gun was fixed to the right hand side, and swung forward to allow the gunner to push in a charger of twenty rounds. The magazine was then swung back to close, and the rounds fed in the normal way. The idea of a fixed maga- zine exercised many designers in the years after the First World War, as it seems to offer advantages over the more usual removable box. For one thing it can be properly machined, and so should not jam so frequently; for another it means that only one magazine needs to be carried, that is the one on the gun; and finally, it can be loaded with loose ammunition

145

taken from the riflemen of the squad. Like everything else, there are two sides to the question and the drawbacks outweigh the gains. The bulk and weight on the guns is a distinct disadvantage; if the magazine picks up dust and dirt it is usually difficult to clean it, and while doing so the gun is not firing, and finally loading is generally slower than by simply replacing a box magazine or changing a belt. In actual use the fixed type seems to give just as many jams as the removable, which makes the argument against it even more damning. No matter, the Breda was the standard light gun for the Italian infantry throughout the war, after which it was quietly dropped.

The support machine guns in the Italian army were varied and sometimes strange. Still in service in 1940 was the venerable Fiat Revelli of 1914. This gun looked something like a Maxim in that it had a water cooled barrel of the usual sort of shape, and a square receiver behind it, and was mounted on a tripod. But the resemblance ended there. The calibre was the underpowered 6.5mm round, and the delayed blowback action was almost exactly the same as the Breda light gun. In fact, the Breda took its action from the Revelli. There was the same oil pump, and a magazine feed instead of the belt which all countries used for support fire guns. The magazine held fifty rounds in ten compartments of five, which cannot have helped in sustained fire missions, and the weight of the whole gun was almost the same as the Maxim derivations, namely just over 40lbs for the gun and another 50 for the tripod. Rate of fire was low at 400 to 500 a minute, and all in all it does not seem a very good return for the effort of manufacture and manning. It was brought up to date in 1935 with the Model 35. Some Model 1914s were converted, and some 35s were new manufacture. The barrel was air cooled, and could be changed. It needed to be, as it was not really

heavy enough for the job and heate quickly. The magazine was replace by a belt, which was a step in th right direction, and the oil pump wa dropped. In its place the chambe was fluted so that the cartridge would not stick to the sides, but sa to relate, they still did, and som guns had the oiling equipment reir stated. Another charming featur inherited from the Model 1914 was a operating rod which ran outside th top of the receiver and buffered again a block just above the handgrip What stroke of genius prompte Revelli to leave this rod uncovere one can only guess at, but it does n require much imagination to see wh; happened to gunners whose finge strayed during firing. The Model had another curious feature in that fired from a closed bolt. Thus, whe the trigger was released at the end a burst, the bolt closed onto a fre round and rammed it into the h chamber. If the barrel was anythi like warm it was only a matter time before the round 'cooked o with consequent hazard to a friendly troops walking in front, a also to the gunner who might doing a little maintenance to t gun, or even clearing some jam. A let us not forget that evil operati rod, poised on top of the receiver trap the unwary. Not a pleasant g at all! Taking all the features of bo guns, the Model 1914 was probably t better of the two.

The Revelli models were supp mented by a Breda design of t middle 1930s. This was the Model which came in 8mm. It was a sensib strong weapon which came throu the war with good reports (ev likely, look at the other choice but even so was not quite like a other gun. The oil pump was on again a feature, needed here for t same reason as with the othe

**An Italian Fiat 8mm (Revelli) model 3 machine gun in readyness against enemy aircraft**

**British troops turn an 8mm Breda on the Italians from whom it was seized**

namely that the cartridges were not given an initial tug with a good mechanical advantage to loosen them in the chamber. For some inexplicable reason no Italian gun did this, although it was well known for years as being necessary for smooth operation, and they all pulled the case direct out and away to the ejector. One step forward was the fact that more power was available from using gas operation. The feed system was almost unique, in that the rounds were fed in from little trays or flat magazines inserted from the side, and having fired the cartridge, the gun then replaced the empty case into the tray, and pushed the whole thing out of the other side, thus ensuring maximum tidiness on the battlefield, if little else. Quite apart from the additional mechanical effort and jiggery-pokery to put the cases back into the tray, anyone trying to reload a tray

had to remove the empties first. Bu the ways of the Italian machine gu designers were ever devious.

All in all, the Italian machine gu picture of the Second World War difficult to explain. It is easy to pol fun at the designs, they were u doubtedly odd, and it must have bee obvious to the troops that design an performance were poor, and all tl more obvious once battle was joine Italy took an enthusiastic part in tl Spanish Civil War and had a goc opportunity to try out weapons ar ideas. Mussolini was a semi-militai dictator and one presumes that l would have had an interest in tl army's equipment, but it seems nc As we have seen from what happenc with Hitler, it is sometimes not good thing if your dictator gets tc interested in weaponry, and possib Mussolini was sensible enough believe his advisers and not interfei Finally, one can only question how was that a country renowned for tl design and manufacture of wor beating cars, ships, and aeroplanes could produce such a poor and uninspired selection of small arms.

Having slated Italy for poor weapons, we can now turn to Japan and continue the process, because here again was a diversity of thought and manufacture that led to a whole series of unsatisfactory machine guns which the Japanese soldier was forced to use, though whether the war would have ended any differently had the imperial army had a proper family of small arms is doubtful; it would probably just have been more difficult for the Allies and might have taken a very little longer. The outstanding feature of the prewar procurement policy for Japanese machine guns is a total lack of coordination between interested parties, and, to a lesser extent, an almost deliberate avoidance of logic and progress. The following brief survey will, it is hoped, be capable of comprehension without too much effort, but it has been much simplified in order that it shall be. The reader will have had some experience of Japanese numbering and nomenclature by now, but among the machine guns it reaches a level of complexity which one hopes confused even the Japanese, for it leaves the researcher reeling. It all started from the French Hotchkiss, which was taken up in Japan after the Russo-Japanese war of 1905. The later 1914 model was also adopted and modified by General Nambu, who did much work in Japanese armaments. We will now skip the next logical step which is to describe the Hotchkiss, and return to when discussing support or medium machine guns.

Starting with light machine guns, the standard model for many years before the war, and during the war also, was the Type 11, designed by Nambu and brought into service in 1922. Like all Japanese guns, there is

Japanese troops in action against the Chinese utilising 6.5mm Nambu Type II (1922) light machine guns

something ungainly about the Type 11, mostly contributed by the butt. The barrel was finned, there was a long pair of bipod legs at the muzzle, a large square receiver, and a wooden butt that looks for all the world like a ship's rudder all set for a sharp turn to starboard. The small of the butt is very thin, and made of steel, while the shoulder part is deep and square, giving the rudder effect, and is offset to the right to bring the line of sight in front of the firer's face. But there are other oddities to the Type 11. The most striking is the feed mechanism. The gun has a hopper on the left hand side in which are fed clips of five rounds. These clips are the ones used for the Ariska rifle and they are loaded in lying on their sides. The feed mechanism of the gun took each clip and stripped out the rounds, ejecting case and clip to the right. The idea is marvellous, because there is no need for specially packed ammunition for the gun, but like all other obvious advantages, it never works out that way in practice, and the payment for this feature comes in the fact that stoppages were frequent, and the rate of fire had to remain at a modest level otherwise the feed mechanism could not keep up. Another drawback to the Type 11, and it shared this with several other Japanese guns, was that like the Italians, the ammunition needed to be oiled as there was once again no primary extraction. Oiled cartridges and all those little fingers stripping the clips meant dirt collection, and consequent jams. Mechanical complication very rarely pays off.

The Type 11 was also used in tanks, when it had a larger feed hopper, and was called the Type 91. It nearly always carried a long telescope sight almost as big as the barrel, and appeared with a bipod for infantry use. The hopper feed must have been quite useless to a tank crew, so a change was made and another gun issued, this time with a magazine feed. Here the Japanese scored an unquestioned first, for no other country inflicted a gun on its tank crews where the ammunition feed was by means of a box magazine. The gun was a straight copy of the Czech ZB 26, and as no other was produced in time to replace it, it lasted the war out. It was called the Type 97, but before it came the Type 96, which was a jazzed up Type 11. It had a box magazine holding 30 rounds of 6.5mm ammunition, a quick change barrel, and no oiler. But the oil was still there, it came when loading, from an oiler built into the magazine loader, so the advance was not all that noticeable. After this, three years later in 1939, came the Type 99, a much better gun, although not significantly different in outline from the Type 96. It had no need for oiled cartridges, and fired the 7.7mm round. It was rather heavy for a light machine gun, turning the scales at $24\frac{1}{2}$lbs, although for this weight one got a 1.5 times telescopic sight. Most of the service guns had a copy of the Czech drum backsight similar to the Bren. It became the standard service light machine gun of the Japanese infantry, although there is much doubt as to exactly how many units were fully equipped with it before the war ended. In December 1943 it was described as being one of the newer guns to be met in action in the Pacific and, bearing in mind the fact that the Japanese factories never managed to keep up with demand, it seems highly unlikely that Type 99s were issued in large quantities before 1945. One maddening feature of the Type 99 is that the round which it fires is not the same as the 7.7mm one fired by the Type 92 support machine gun (of which more in a moment). A more confusing state of affairs it would be difficult to imagine, but there was one more twisted bit of thinking which will be explained later.

There were several other types of guns in service throughout the Japanese forces, which it is unnecessary to spend long in describing. All were copies, with and without the manufacturers' permission, of guns in

*Above:* A direct copy of the ZB26; the Japanese 7.7mm light machine gun Type 99 (1939). *Below:* British troops in pre- and post-1943 type steel helmets man a French 8mm M1914 Hotchkiss MG on a 1916 tripod

Nambu type 92 machine gun; *Calibre:* 7.7mm; *System of Operation:* Gas, Automatic only; *Length:* 45.5 inches; *Barrel Length:* Approx 29 inches; *Feed Device:* 30 Round strip; *Front Sights:* Barleycorn with protecting ears; *Rear Sights:* Tangent with aperture or telescope; *Weight:* 122 lbs with tripod; *Muzzle Velocity:* Approx 2,400 feet per second; *Cyclic Rate:* 450-500 rpm

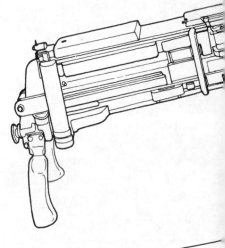

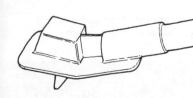

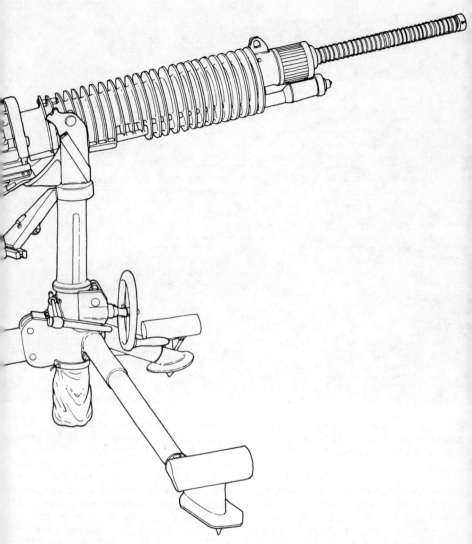

**US forces utilising a Japanese
7.7mm type 92 machine gun
in the Pacific**

service in the West. For instance, the
navy and naval air corps used copies
of Lewis guns, calling them Type 92,
and there were copies of Vickers,
Browning, Hotchkiss, and MG 15, to
list but a few. There was an element of
standardization in that most most of
this motley was chambered for the
7.7mm (.303-inch) round, but not all of

it was by any means. One wonders
how they fought a war at all.

Finally, to the Japanese medium, or
support machine guns. The reader
should take heart here because the
picture is nothing like as confused,
apart from names, as with the light
machine guns. The standard weapon
was the 1932 Type 92, a direct descen-
dant of the Hotchkiss, and firing
7.7mm (.303-inch) ammunition. It was
a heavy, gas operated gun, mounted
on a tripod, and air cooled. By its

**Chinese troops armed with the French Chatellrault 7.5mm 1924 M 29 machine gun, also known as the FM 24/29**

slow rate of fire it earned itself the name of 'woodpecker' from the Allies, and it still exists because not many years ago one was heard and recognised firing across the border towards Hong Kong from Communist China. In 1937 the need for a lighter version was stated, and resulted in the Type 1, which came out in 1942. The differences between the two are slight, except for weight, although the barrel of the later gun is more easily removed, and it only uses the later type of 7.7mm ammunition. The Type 92 fires the semi-rimmed 7.7mm round, which in the later series of guns became a rimless round which cannot be fed into the earlier guns, but the earlier ammunition does go into the later

guns, if you follow. One hopes that someone did, because with all that complication the business of ammunition supply must have been a nightmare. And we realise now that we forgot to draw attention to the fact that at one time there were two machine guns called Type 92 in service at the same time. One was the infantry gun just described, and the other the Naval Lewis, mentioned earlier.

Both the support guns were Hotchkiss derivations, and both used the odd Hotchkiss method of ammunition feed by means of a metal strip holding thirty rounds, not a satisfactory arrangement for any but a light gun, and not much good then as they are so liable to damage. Another curiosity of the Japanese guns worth a mention was the habit of making sockets in the tripod legs so that the gun crew could push poles into them and so

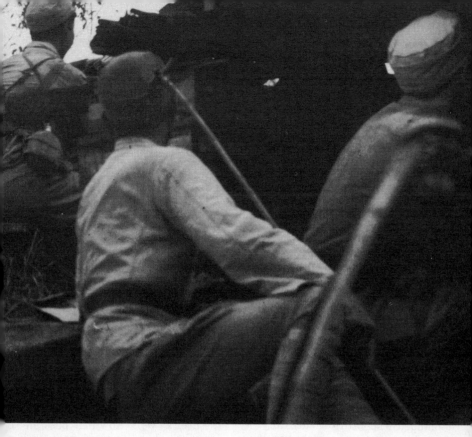

carry the gun for short distances between two men like a litter. Not a bad idea if you do not want to go far.

The final episode in the machine gun saga covers the French contribution. Like so many other nations, the French weapons of 1939 were not markedly different from those of 1919, and their machine guns were no exception. The squad light gun was a 1924 design modified in 1929 to fire the 7.5mm round. It was a fairly workmanlike gun, said to have been inspired by the Browning Automatic Rifle, which it outwardly resembles in some ways. But the magazine is on top of the receiver, carrying twenty-five rounds, and the all-up weight is higher. In addition to a bipod, there is a monopod below the butt, a curiosity which is only found otherwise on the Japanese Type 99, and which in neither case offers much advantage

to the user. The idea is to give some ability to lay a fixed line for defensive firing, but it is largely illusory. Another strange feature is a double trigger, one for single shots and one for automatic. This gun, known as the Model 1924 M 29, is still in service in parts of the old French Colonial Empire, and is apparently well liked for its simplicity and reliability. The medium machine gun was, of course, the Hotchkiss, and it hardly differed in form or performance from those used by the Japanese except in that it could be fed with a belt which consisted of multiples of the 30-round strip. Its use as a first line weapon in the French army finished in 1940, and it never reappeared after the war in any numbers, although it remained with some other countries, particularly in eastern parts of the world, until very recently.

155

# Unusual weapons 'from the drawing board'

The oddities of life are always interesting, and odd small arms are more interesting than most things. Wars are great breeding grounds for inventors, and it is sometimes quite extraordinary to see what strange devices are produced by them. Stranger still is the tactical thinking which goes behind the use, or suggested use, of the more esoteric gadgets. Most of the inventions which appeared for infantry weapons seemed to envisage the user being in an already desperate situation which demanded desperate measures anyway to get him out alive, and the resulting invention is pretty alarming to use and not always entirely safe. One gets the impression that the inventor has read a few lurid comic books of infantry battles, and based his judgement on that. But all wars breed these ideas, and most of them must be a continual source of irritation to their appropriate service departments.

Continuing the theme of the tight corner and how to get out of it, a real winner was suggested in the USA, allegedly from within the navy. This was a large and heavy leather glove with a crude form of gun rivetted onto the back. This gun was so simple that it hardly merits the name at all, but it was a holder which contained a Smith and Wesson .38 cartridge and, in general shape, was flat and rectangular. A steel plunger projected from the front end of it, and this was the strike release. The bullet had no

barrel as such to travel up, it was launched directly from the breech. The idea was to use the glove as a sort of knuckle duster, and do as much damage as possible by hitting with the 'gun' using a backhand swing. It was felt that this would do to crack a skull at least, but if the opponent refused to give up under that sort of attack, or, as the official document put it, 'in an emergency', the striker was rammed into the opponent, and the .38 fired into him. This would obviously finish him off – and no doubt the firer as well. How it is possible to describe a hand-to-hand fight with a war enemy as a situation which is anything else than 'an emergency' is beyond the author, and the results of firing a gun sewn to one's glove tax the imagination no less. The difficulties accompanying the use of such a weapon are really too obvious to bother with, but one does wonder how the inventor intended the user to be certain that he always had his glove gun with him. Did he wear it throughout the summer?

In the same category was the .22 pistol made to look like a pocket propelling pencil. This was a special assassination weapon, and not really an infantry gun at all, but it illustrates the trends of thought that some inventors follow. It was meant to be a last-ditch close quarter device, fired by pulling back the spring clip and letting it drive forward under a spring to fire a single .22 cartridge sitting in the end of a short barrel. Holding such a thing would be extremely difficult, and aiming it even more so. It was made in small quantities, and it was carried by a few men. Apparently none of these used it in anger, and one managed to shoot himself in the foot with it. So at least it worked.

Not quite in the same category was a .45-inch single shot pistol which it is reported was made in quite large numbers and actually used in combat. It was a crude and ugly brute for use by native guerillas in the Pacific and Asian theatre of war. It was a really basic weapon, made in the rough shape of an automatic pistol. The stubby barrel was simply a plain piece of tube with no rifling, and a simple breech closure. The metal butt was hollow and held a few spare rounds. The empty case was ejected by pushing a short stick down the barrel, and there were naturally no safety devices. It was given to friendly natives together with a comic strip set of pictures showing how to use it, and they were left to get on with it. It is reported to have been remarkably effective, not least because the firer did not dare miss; he fired his shot and made himself scarce immediately.

Such gadgets as these pistols will turn up in any war, and there will always be someone who will authorise their manufacture on a small scale, but their value is almost nil.

Other ideas are more practical, and the Germans had a few of these. Probably the most famous special weapon of the German infantry was the curved barrel attachment for the MP 43 and 44. It is not now clear what prompted this idea in the first place, but some reports say that it arose from street fighting in Italy when the troops asked for a gun to shoot round corners, and others that it was meant for tanks and armoured cars so that the crews could shoot over the sides or out of pistol ports and clear away enemy infantry, particularly Russian infantry, who crouched close up and

out of reach of normal fire. This last theory seems a bit far fetched, as the attachment is bigger than any pistol port in a tank, but it just might have been of some value if fired from the sides of the half-tracks and three-quarter-tracks of the Panzer Grenadiers. As for street fighting, well that is anybody's guess; just how often does one have to shoot round a corner? No matter, the curved barrel attachment was made, and made in reasonable numbers. The first version turned the bullet through thirty degrees by simply adding a short length of curved barrel onto the muzzle of the MP 43, and clamping it in place. Some holes were drilled in the beginning of the bend to allow some gas to escape and so slow the bullet a little, (after all, range was not important), and a fairly bulky periscopic type of sight stuck up above. The shooter looked forward into a square of glass in the sight and saw a backsight and a foresight which he lined up onto the target. These sights were not the normal rifle ones, but were special ones in the periscope. Firing the rifle caused no particularly unusual movement apart from an upwards recoil, and the bullet was shot out at exactly thirty degrees to the original line of the barrel. It was most ingenious, and quite successful, if you want that sort of thing. It only worked with the Kurz round, and attempts to fit it to the normal 7.92mm ammunition ended in trouble because the higher power of the round caused very rapid erosion of the curved part. Even with the Kurz there was a strictly limited life to the curve, but one does not imagine that such a device would fire many shots in an action. A ninety degree version was also made in very small numbers, but with this the erosion problems were severe, and it was not entirely satisfactory when the war ended. Some effort must have gone into designing and making these attachments, and it is hard to see that it was well spent. Really it is one more example of the

Another idea goes through the trial
stage, this time a Browning with
periscope attachment

way in which the German war machine
wasted its resources on useless complication, when a rational approach
would have paid better dividends.

In Britain there was just as much
useless invention as anywhere else.
One glorious theory concerned filling
anti-aircraft shells with luminous
paint so that enemy aircraft would be
sprayed with it, and so made visible
to the night fighters who would then
shoot them down. The hero who
thought of that one was not a bit
pleased when Whitehall suggested
that bits of steel were a better spray-
ing agent than paint.

But to get back to the point. A gun
which never saw service was the
Welgun sub-machine gun, produced
in 1943. This was one of several attempts to improve the Sten, and the
Welgun proposed to do it by being
shorter and lighter. Nowadays a great
many of the latest sub-machine guns
use the principles which the Welgun
pioneered, the heart of the idea being
to make the bolt hollow, so that it
could pass over the breech end of
the barrel when pushing in the round,
and so have its main weight in front
of the breech. In itself this does not
matter and it means that there is
much less space needed in the back
end of the receiver. The empty case is

ejected through a slot in the bolt side,
and in the case of the Welgun a further
refinement was to put the return
spring in front of it, and wrapped
around the barrel. Using a Sten
barrel and spring and a neat folding
butt the overall length was only
seventeen inches. The magazine was
Sten, which might have given trouble,
and it fed upwards, acting as a forward hand grip as well. All told, it
looks a promising idea which might
have been a worthwhile weapon.
Only one was made.

But it was the British Home Guard
which really beat the band for out-
rageous ideas. Any special force will
modify the government's weapons to
some extent, but when the government
does not hand out anything beyond a
few rifles, and then gives to the rifle-
less ones a weapon which went out of
date in the 17th Century, can you
wonder that some men went home
and dug out dad's shot gun? It is a
fact that several thousand pikes were
made in 1940 and 1941, and given to
those Home Guard platoons which
were short of rifles and bayonets, and
that means most of them. Let us be
fair, though, the 1940 pike was a bit
different from the 1640 model – it was
shorter. You had to get a bit closer to
kill the chap, and you did not have
the benefit of a breastplate or a bit of
chain mail either. The issue pike was
supposed to be the same length as a
rifle with the bayonet fixed, and so it

**The rifle which can 'fire round corners'. The German MP 44 with curved barrel and periscope attachment**

was to be used in the same way as for bayonet fighting. Just as well really, as there were not too many books on pike drill left at the time. It was made by welding the SMLE bayonet into a length of water pipe, and fortunately there were plenty of bayonets – most of them pre-SMLE. There was a certain amount of embarrassment in official circles about the pike, and it was dropped as soon as decently possible, but not before passing into English legend, and also into Home Guard armouries where some were still to be seen in the 1950s.

Yet another weapon of the desperate days of 1940 was the anti-tank petrol squad. Let it be understood that these existed, and were trained after a fashion, but were never used, and so far as can be discovered, never actually practised their routine on a tank; it was all theory. The whole thing was due to the Spanish Civil War, when German and Italian tanks had a hard time when they came up against the Spanish Asturian miners. These men were determined fighters, and by skilful use of ground and mining explosives they made a significant effect on the tanks. Those who had fought in Spain brought the idea home, and in many a village and town in England the anti-tank petrol squad was formed

in imitation of the Spaniards. Three men made up the team: number one carried a strong iron bar, or a short piece of railroad line (actually a very short piece, because anyone who has lifted railroad line will know what it weighs): number two had a blanket and some fuze matches or a Verey pistol, or some other reliable way of making a flame: number three had a bucket of petrol.

The pattern of attack was this. The three men lurked behind a corner, it being necessary to launch this type of attack only in a built up area. It did not work in fields, though it was hoped that some way of doing it might be found. When a tank came down the road they waited until it was abreast of them. By now riflemen would have ensured that the tank had had to close down, and so it would be blind and, hopefully, cautious as it drew level, Number one leapt out and thrust his iron bar into the tracks close to the sprocket, thus stopping the tank. Number two immediately hurled his blanket into the stationary tracks. Number three flung his petrol over the blanket, and number two set light to it. All three retired to their corner, and the tank blazed.

Simple isn't it? Just as well it was never tried. To get this sequence I interviewed a man who had actually been the number two in a squad in the local town to me; he says he never felt altogether confident about the idea.

# Bibliography

*Pistols, Rifles and Machine Guns* by W G B Allen (Oxford University Press, London. Borden Publishing, Alhambra, California)
*Small Arms of the World* by J E Smith (Stacpole Books, Harrisburg, Pennsylvania)
*The Lee Enfield Rifle* by E G B Reynolds (Herbert & Jenkins, London. Arco Publishing, New York)
*The Longest Retreat* by Tim Carew (Hamish Hamilton, London)
*German Infantry Weapons of World War II* by A J Barker (Arms & Armour Press, London)
*Allied Infantry Weapons of World War II* by A J Barker (Arms & Armour Press, London)
*The World's Assault Rifles* by Musgrave and Nelson (TBN Enterprises, Alexandria, Virgina)